Paper

By

Julie Ann Rees

Black Bee Books Ltd.

First Published in Great Britain in 2022 by
Black Bee Books Ltd
Bryn Heulog
Talley
Llandeilo
Wales SA19 7YH

Cover Image © Viktoria Karpunina / Shutterstock.com
Cover Design © Huw Francis

ISBN: 978-1-913853-08-2 (Paperback)
ISBN: 978-1-913853-09-9 (eBook)

www.blackbeebooks.wales

Acknowledgements

This book has been a cathartic journey where some great people have held my hand along the way.

Firstly my thanks go to my university lecturers from the University of Wales Trinity Saint David: Dr. Dick Edwards, Dr Jenni Williams and Dr. Paul Wright, for confidently setting me forth on my creative path and enabling me to believe I can give this writing malarkey a go. Also thanks to my good friend Carly Holmes, a brilliant author herself, for help with early edits, her inspiration and selfless support, and belief in Paper Horses. And to Seonaid from Black Bee Books for giving Paper Horses a chance and helping me shape the final draft and releasing it into the world.

Also huge thanks to my wonderful family and friends especially my Mum for her continued support and my Dad who has since sadly passed away. I finally grabbed that mug Dad!

Many thanks go to Lyndon for trawling through the very first draft and offering much needed advice, and for being a critical ear to everything I write by putting up with me reading my stories out loud.

And last but not least eternal thanks to Elana for just being herself, my horses for being such wondrous beasts and to Spook for comfy cat cuddles and keeping my lap warm.

Dedication

For my daughter

Prologue

Hell

The cell was hot and airless. I sat rigid, trying not to touch anything. Far too weary to stand I perched on the points of my seat bones, muscles clenched. Brown splatters, either shit or blood, stained the walls and the stench of ammonia stung my eyes. They had handcuffed me. I'd flinched as the cold metal clamped around my wrists, trapping me, restraining me. Controlling me. I tried to think what he had done to make this happen. Thank God Susan had arrived on time to take Tessa to safety.

I kept seeing her little face as she pleaded with the French police to not take her Mummy away. On the aeroplane she had drawn me a picture on a scrap of paper, a woman in a long dress astride a rearing horse. "It's you, Mummy," she'd told me, "riding Caramello." My heart missed a beat like it did every time I thought of my beautiful horses. I had that piece of paper my first night in the cell. I slept with it lying next to my face on the stinking pillow. Now they had taken it from me. Tessa's little drawing.

I closed my eyes and felt tears struggling to form under my dry swollen eyelids, but I had cried every ounce of liquid from my body. I thought I had escaped him but I was trapped in his tentacles again. Anguish howled inside my head like wolves and I wondered if they would pad down the corridor to peer through the bars and taunt and terrify me. Large misshapen fairytale wolves where, as a child, wild eyed and innocent, I'd listen to scary stories embracing the fear, but deep down knowing I was safe and protected from such wicked creatures… but not anymore.

I'd had an idyllic and happy childhood. I'd been lucky, privileged even, so what clues were there in the choices I'd made, the places I'd been and the dreams I'd run after that could explain how I'd ended up here? I remembered my first Christmas as a child at our new house, and a nightmare that now seemed familiar. I thought of my family and friends and prayed to any God who'd listen that they'd be able to get my beautiful daughter home to Wales. My beloved Wales and where my journey began.

Finding Magic: Christmas

I was eight years old and it was Christmas. We had not long moved to a new house, a Victorian residence, built on the site of an older dwelling dating back to 1743. The house as it stands today was built in 1846. Tall, elegant and white with dark olive stone frames complimenting the sash windows. It was cold, damp and needed lots of work, but I loved it because it had a paddock where I planned to keep a pony.

The house breathed and came alive when we moved in, and expelled a soft contented sigh when the Christmas tree lights twinkled into life after several failed attempts. The tree for our first Christmas was the largest ever. My sister and I had gone with my father to the forestry commission where he sold his chain saws, and together we chose the biggest, most regal looking tree we could find. My parents cursed and struggled whilst a suitable stand was found to support it before bringing it into the hall.

The top brushed the ceiling leaving hardly any room for the fairy, which hung slightly lopsided, but nobody cared. The tree outshone any of the decorations. It was magical and the smell of pine was glorious. It flooded the hallway and crept up the stairs to give us dreams of myth and fairy tale from deep Nordic forests. I'd sit on the stairs in the evenings before my parents went to bed and stare at the mighty pine. My eyelids, heavy with sleep, blinked as the fairy lights twinkled into colourful orbs and floated up the stairs towards me.

When asked what we wanted for Christmas the answer my sister and I always gave was, a pony. We couldn't have one, but this time our parents had agreed to seriously consider the matter in the New Year. In the meantime we made coloured paper horse decorations, which trotted and galloped enticingly around the house, jumping paper chain garlands and knocking over cards. I imagined what colour my horse would be as I drew manes and tails onto the paper horses and watched them spring to life. I wondered how to go about the next stage of parent nagging, this time for a pony each, because my sister and I both knew sharing would be catastrophic. Christmas Eve arrived and after having exhausted myself and the dog by hiding her present in different places around the house – she was excellent at retrieving it – I went to bed. The faster I could get to sleep, the quicker the morning would come. Although I'd been daydreaming I was a warrior and my paper horse a trusty steed, I did not expect the dream that came before dawn.

A dark haired woman sits astride a blood bay horse with an abundance of black mane. A storm roars, battering her. I cannot see her face. Her head is tilted downwards, braced against the wind goblins that shriek and pull her hair into a ragged halo. Strong hands cling to the horse's mane as she struggles to keep her seat. The wind is deafening, like white noise on a television with the sound on full. The horse, ears back, nostrils taut and eyes half closed, holds his ground against the onslaught of weather. They stand upon a wasteland, vast and frozen. Patches of frosted earth succumb to black peat bogs, hiding the ancient remains of victims. Like a knight on a chessboard, joined together as one, they face a stone tower.

The tower is beautiful and terrifying – Rapunzel's prison or Bluebeard's keep. Poison ivy clings to the stone and deadly nightshade peeps from behind the dark green leaves; the deadly kiss disguised by violet beauty. Near the top a window blinks with a flickering glow. Moving away from the storm that centres on the woman and horse, I drift towards the light. A child is crying. The sound of her anguish echoes from the bottom of the tower to float in the air around me as grey clouds. Gathering in strength they fuel the storm that rages against the lady knight. The horse lowers its head and together they push forward a few paces as if they too can hear the cries. I hesitate. Fear's bony fingers poke my chest but I have to see the source of the crying even though every nerve screams against it. Ignoring the terror that fights to prevent me, I look through the window.

Smooth granite walls glistening with moisture plummet towards the light source. On the floor lays a child, a single candle burning beside her. Dark hair falls in knotted tendrils over her tiny frame that shudders with every sob. The sobs form a column of clouds that billow towards the window. Each one holds a cry for help so pitiful that tears begin to fall unchecked down my cheeks. I watch this

3

stream of distress feed the angry storm. The wind goblins laugh as they gorge on it. How much more can the woman and horse endure? I have to tell the child to stop crying. I have to comfort the child and reassure her help is just outside. "Please, little girl," I call out tentatively. "It's going to be all right." She stops abruptly and slowly lifts her head, pushing up onto her hands and turning to look straight into my eyes. It is me. It is my own face looking back, broken and twisted in pain. I recoil and a piercing neigh draws my eyes back to the lady knight. Slowly, she too lifts her head.

I began to fall and woke with a jerk. The bedclothes twisted around me wet with sweat. Suddenly I sat bolt upright. It was Christmas! I didn't forget the dream but pushed it firmly to the back of my mind, where it surfaced years later. Leaping out of bed I ran to the top of the stairs and looked down at the tree. There were presents underneath. It was still dark and the house was silent except for the paper horses that cavorted around the hall nuzzling each other playfully. I stretched out my fingers towards a bright red one, the stallion. The felt tip pen I'd drawn his mane with floated around him in strands of inky black. He tossed his head and was about to let me stroke him when a yellow mare distracted him. She was nibbling the dress of the lopsided fairy who was unsuccessfully shooing it with her wand.

I plugged in the tree lights and went to sit on the stairs. I wasn't in a hurry to open my presents. Instead, I wanted to savour this magical moment and watch the paper horses dance and play. The red stallion herded the yellow mare back towards a group of green and blue ones. The red and yellow fitted beautifully in between. Dawn was fast approaching and part of me longed for this moment to never end. The uneasy feeling the nightmare had left was now forgotten and I was the happiest little girl in the world. I watched as Christmas Eve gathered up her long elegant skirts and got ready to leave until next year. She smiled at me as she waited patiently by the door. The first rays of sun stretched pink across the sky and with a warm jovial guffaw, Christmas Day arrived.

Smokey

The New Year rolled in on the back of a cold wet January, and the Christmas decorations, including the paper horses, were packed safely away. It didn't dampen my spirits as I couldn't wait for the first signs of spring and the promise of a real horse to become a reality. Soon the first tiny white snowdrops unveiled their shy faces, followed by glorious daffodils that engulfed the flower borders and hedgerows with their bright yellow splendour. Spring had arrived and my sister had taken over the local evening paper as soon as it was delivered. She frantically opened it to the classifieds, and with me peering over her shoulder, we scanned the livestock horses and ponies section.

This resulted in immediate friction. I dreamt of a sensible pony who would take care of me as much as I would them. I had idyllic visions of hacking to local gymkhanas, winning rosettes and trophies, much like in the short stories I'd read in the horse and pony magazines so popular at the time. My sister, however, being five years my senior and more confident, if not reckless, hankered after a golden beast with flaring nostrils and billowing mane. My sister won. Even though the golden horse refused to enter the horse trailer and the seller had to ride him to our house, Sunnyboy was purchased.

Sunnyboy was a four-year-old part Arab Welsh cob, recently broken, completely unschooled and extremely unsuitable. He was also a rig – which meant he hadn't been gelded properly and behaved like a stallion around other horses, screaming and threatening to kick. But the most exciting thing in my sister's eyes was that he was a horse – not a pony – and a beautiful golden palomino colour. The first time she placed the saddle on his back resulted in a series of bucks, until it plummeted to the ground. After having it shown to him he decided to accept it, although the bridle was a different matter. He refused to open his mouth for the bit and held his head high out of her reach. My sister tried and tried until eventually Mum had the bright idea of smearing it in honey. He also panicked when she tied his lead rein to the gate, breaking the gate and galloping off across the field. When she attempted to catch him he kicked her, leaving a hoof print in her thigh.

Eventually, successfully saddled and bridled, my sister went for her first of many rides on her wonderful but highly strung Sunnyboy. I was left standing alone in the yard in tears. To ease my grief she agreed to take me with her, perched on the front of the saddle. We rode for miles like this, two skinny kids wedged into the same saddle, exploring the mountain on a horse that chose to go wherever he wanted. My mother began to worry and would drive out in the car trying to find us. This was futile; we were miles off any road, but one day she spotted us. To her horror she saw a tiny figure of a horse with two tinier figures on top, clinging for dear life, galloping wildly across a distant hilltop.

My mother was beginning to realise that I needed my own sensible pony, one suitable for a child. A local showing yard was advertising three ponies for sale. Their names were Butterfly, Lucy and Smokey. We went to see them. Butterfly was a beautiful show pony, a Barbie doll of the equine world, and far too expensive. Lucy was within budget, but she was newly broken and highly strung; we had learnt a lesson with Sunnyboy, so she too was discarded. This left Smokey. She was fat and round and completely different to the other two. Where the coats of the others were smooth and shiny, hers was rough and coarse. She didn't shine like Butterfly who was a deep mahogany bay, or gleam like Lucy's dark iron grey. She was just a dirty yellowy white with a wiry grey mane that resembled a toilet brush.

Fear Wolves and Boggarts

Smokey was now my pony. The sheer thrill of this left me unable to concentrate on anything else. I was expected to take care of her myself, which was a big responsibility and a lot of hard work. I embraced it, and couldn't wait for the weekend and my first ride out.

Friday night I went to bed happy and excited about the next day's ride, but I dreamt I could hear wolves howling outside. The menacing wails struck me with fear. I got up and peered out of my bedroom window and there just below sat a cluster of large grey wolves staring up at me. These were not like normal wolves I'd seen on wildlife programmes, but were hunched and awkward. They looked like an illustration of the Big Bad Wolf from Little Red Riding Hood. The largest looked straight at me; his sinister gaze held mine, preventing me from turning away. I awoke, trembling.

I lay awake feeling apprehensive; even though I was excited, I was also nervous about my first ride out. I got dressed into my riding jodhpurs and went downstairs for breakfast. I'd groomed Smokey a couple of times and discovered she didn't like me brushing her tail – or picking up her feet to clean her hooves. I caught her and led her to the gate. My sister was also preparing Sunnyboy so she could come with me.

"Get the hoof pick and clean her feet," ordered my sister. I managed the front two and gingerly approached her hind legs. I tapped them gently, leaning my weight in towards her hoping she would raise her hoof. She stamped it towards me instead. I tried again and she swung her quarters towards me, knocking me to the floor. She looked at me, obviously thinking what a pushover I was. "Be firm with her," said my sister. "She'll walk all over you otherwise. Are you scared?"

"No," I snapped back a little too defensively. "Of course I'm not." My sister watched as I got up and approached Smokey's hind legs again – and again, the same thing happened.

"Yes you are," she said spitefully, "you're shaking like a leaf." She laughed, took the hoof pick from me and picked out

Smokey's hooves with ease. "See, easy when you know how, brush her tail – it's full of burrs," she said. I began to brush the beautiful thick grey tail that was knotted and tangled. Immediately Smokey looked back at me warningly and raised her hind leg. I stopped brushing and just picked the burrs out with my fingers; my sister didn't notice, thankfully. I placed the saddle on her back and was relieved to have no bucking bronco antics although I suffered a sharp nip on my bottom when I did the girth up. I managed to bridle her too. Maybe there was no need for me to be so nervous after all.

I stood on the mounting block and much to my shock I noticed my legs were shaking. Mum had come down to watch and I hastily smiled and jumped with false bravado into the saddle. Smokey didn't move and I tapped her neck and said good girl, but my voice was a terrified croak. My sister mounted Sunnyboy and clipped a leading rein onto Smokey just in case. We waved to Mum as we left. Soon, we discovered that being on a lead rein was not at all easy. Sunnyboy tried to kick Smokey and Smokey squealed in anger, tossing her head. I had no control at all. At the cattle grid before the mountain, my sister undid the lead rein. "She'll follow," she said. "And don't fall off!" I nodded.

All went well to begin with. Smokey was a wise little pony and knew what she was doing. My sister turned onto what I called the yellow mountain. A vast landscape of bleak Welsh moorland dotted here and there with lethal peat bogs. I knew this land because I had experienced it before on Sunnyboy, but I'd had my eyes tightly closed and relied on my sister to control matters. This was different. I felt Smokey begin to jog eagerly and she yanked at the reins, pulling them from my hands and unseating me in the saddle. The wind picked up, I thought I heard a wolf howl in the distance and I remembered the wolves in my dream.

My sister set off at a gallop and Smokey sprang forward, determined not to be left behind. The wet sticky mud from Sunnyboys's hooves was thrown backwards. Smokey didn't seem to mind and just lowered her head until her nose was almost on the ground. The worst of the mud missed her but hit me instead. I clung to the front of the saddle. Wind goblins sprang up from all around laughing wickedly at me as the mud splattered my face. I half closed my eyes and turned my head to the side and screamed when I thought I saw a large crooked wolf loping alongside me. Just as I looked forward again I saw Sunnyboy leap into the air to jump over a wide gaping bog. Smokey gathered herself up and leapt with him, luckily clearing it. I felt my body leave the saddle and saw my sister glance back and pull back to a walk. She looked frightened. Luckily I landed back into the saddle as Smokey came back to a walk.

"I think I took the wrong track," she said. "I've never seen that bog before; it's a good job Smokey can jump. Well done for staying on." I couldn't speak and burst into tears. I glanced around nervously for the wolves, but there were no grey shapes following us. We walked back to the peat bog we'd just jumped. It was huge. I couldn't believe Smokey and I had managed to clear it. I saw my sister look at the track which led directly to the bog. I knew we'd not gone the wrong way, and I knew that certain creatures lurked on these moors to lure travellers into danger. Some such creature – maybe a boggart – had moved that treacherous bog into our path. As we headed down off the moors I heard a wicked little laugh echo over the hills behind us.

The fear wolves had won. How they howled with glee outside my bedroom window at night. I was a nervous wreck. I was unable to brush Smokey or pick out her feet and the thought of going for a ride filled me with dread. I stopped riding and taking care of her. I had failed and I hated myself for it. My mother and father both yelled at me, threatening to sell the pony if I didn't get on with the business of riding. I began to dread the weekends and when it rained, I sighed with relief as I wouldn't be expected to ride in the rain. This Saturday, unfortunately, I was awoken by the sun streaming through my window. My sister was going riding with her friend and I was going to have to go too.

I couldn't eat breakfast. My stomach was loose and queasy and I felt sick. I had my jodhpurs on and glanced down at my lap; the very sight of them made me want to faint. I looked up and caught my mother's eye. She looked at me with that all-knowing expression. I ran to the bathroom. As I returned I could hear her talking to my sister.

"Leave her alone. I'll give her a little more time and if she doesn't get back on, then the pony will be sold."

"She'll never ride her, she hasn't got the guts," I heard my sister reply. "Shall I go and fetch her and try getting her out today?"

"No, she'll either wise up or not, just leave her for today, and if she hasn't shown any interest by next weekend that pony will be up for sale."

I froze. I desperately wanted to ride, but was terrified of the yellow mountain and the speed at which my sister and her friend rode. I felt out of my depth and completely overwhelmed. I heard my sister coming towards the door and quickly I ran into the *cwtch dan star,* which is a Welsh phrase for the cupboard under the stairs, but in our house it was almost a small room. I huddled by a pile of boxes beneath the little window that looked out onto the field. It was a lovely day outside. I could hear my sister's footsteps going up the stairs over my head. I could tell she was looking for me, probably to inform me about Smokey being sold if I didn't wise up. I felt physically sick. Her footsteps passed back down and I heard the hall door close once more. Blissfully, I was alone.

Tears began to fall down my cheeks now that I'd avoided being forced to go riding. I wanted to go, but it was such a confusing tangle of emotions. I heard a rustling coming from one of the boxes. Nervously I lifted the cardboard flap and there, much to my delight, was the red paper stallion Christmas decoration I'd made. He trotted out and jumped onto the windowsill tossing his inky mane. I closed my eyes and far into a distant future I felt myself galloping across the yellow mountain on a red bay horse with a long black mane billowing in the wind. I was happy and smiling. My eyes snapped open. I felt a new-found confidence. I didn't need my sister to ride with. I could ride alone, couldn't I?

Outside I heard something panting and a large cloud was gathering, hiding the sun that only moments before had seemed so bright. The red paper stallion turned towards it and stamped his hooves. I cowered in my hiding place. The fear wolves were back to torment me. A freak gust of wind swept against the window, rattling it, and I heard a wicked laugh. The red stallion reared in defiance, and I remembered my dream – the one from Christmas Eve. In that second the bravery of the warrior woman facing the strange tower returned to me and I realised her horse looked much like the paper stallion. I stood up and yelled at the wolves: "Go away, you nasty horrible things!" The stallion reared in support. I was going to do this. I was going to ride Smokey on my own and at my own pace.

"There you are. What on earth is all this shouting about?" said my mother as she swung open the door to the *cwtch dan star*.

"Nothing," I said as I picked up the paper horse, kissed his muzzle and laid him safely back in the box. I felt like a new person. "I'm going out to see Smokey," and strode past my astonished looking mother.

Just baby steps to begin with, I told myself as I caught her and tied her to the gate. It didn't matter if her tail was a mess, I didn't have to brush that today, but I did have to make sure her hooves were free from stones. I took a deep breath and picked out her front hooves with no problem, and then I approached her hind legs. I leaned in towards her and she pushed me with her quarters. Immediately I pushed her back and whilst she was a little off balance I picked up her hind foot, using my hoof pick to scrape out the mud and stones. Without pause I moved onto the other one, and Smokey practically lifted it up for me.

"Good girl!" I said, tapping her neck, and with my new-found confidence I saddled and bridled her. Heading out on my own was still a big step for me so I had a plan. My sister had been using the farmer's old barn to ride in when it rained. She had built little jumps too. Sunnyboy was too big and silly to ride in there safely, so she had been using Smokey. This is where I now led my pony and where I safely climbed into the saddle all on my own. I sat there for a minute savouring the feel of being on my pony. Then slowly I asked her to walk on, and in no time at all I was trotting around the barn and even had a go at one of the tiny jumps. It was an exhilarating experience, and eager to end on a good note, I dismounted and led her back to the gate and gave her carrots and cuddles.

Heading back to the house, I saw my mother. "That was good work," she said. "I was watching from the back bedroom window."

"Really?" I said. I was a little nervous she'd tell me I'd not done enough, and to get out onto the mountain to catch up with my sister, but much to my relief she didn't. I think she realised I needed to do this myself.

The Dwarf Lords

This was just the start of Smokey and my adventures together. We learnt to outrun the fear wolves and the shrieking goblins. Even the wicked moor boggarts on the yellow mountain learned not to play tricks on us. We were protectors of the realm, respected by the high elves in their forest glens and feared by the dwarf lords in their stone castles.

One clear autumn day during school half term I sat on the old stone wall by the vegetable garden and stared at the rows of dying runner bean plants wrapped around the tall sticks, the tasty green beans all gone. I kicked my heels against the wall and remembered Humphrey the pig. When he was a piglet he was easy to cope with, but he grew into a huge boar. He did his job, which was to dig the garden and help clear the land ready for planting, and then he disappeared. I had no idea where he went, but I don't think it was to be a Daddy piggy which is what my mother told me. Poor Humphrey, all he'd wanted was to run free through the fields causing havoc. Sometimes he'd escape and my mum could do nothing until I got home from school to call him.

Every time was the same: standing halfway down the field I'd yell "Humphrey!" He'd lift his huge head, which was a continuation of his giant neck and body, snort with excitement and hurtle towards me. His ears flapped comically in front of his face when he ran, revealing a mischievous pink piggy eye. He'd come trashing through the farmer's fencing causing pregnant cows to run in fear. Then when he was almost upon me, I'd have to run like the devil was on my heels snorting fire and brimstone. It was pandemonium! On reaching the garden wall I'd throw myself onto it just in time, sometimes scraping my knees and elbows on the sharp stones. Once, to Humphrey's utter joy, I left my wellingtons behind in the mud. I laughed as he snorted and snuffled his nose inside them.

My mother would gather up the trailing rope tether attached to his hind leg – this is apparently how you should tether a pig – and he'd look up at me, trying to eat my feet as I dangled them in his face, rubbing his head to distract him as Mum secured him safely. His head felt all bristly and his snout was always wet and covered in mud. He stank too, not an unpleasant smell but earthy and beasty. Up close the glint in his pink beady eyes made him look like he was laughing. I didn't know what he'd do if I failed to make the wall in time. I don't think he knew either, but it was a great game for us both and I loved it as much as he did.

I was restless for adventure sitting on the wall remembering Humphrey, his ghost challenging me to another wild race across the fields. I was bored and needed magic and excitement. I was ten and I had a pony who gave me the power to travel to Middle Earth itself if I so wished. Dad was in the workshop where he lived and Mum was on the phone trying not to get cross. Inspired by Humphrey the pig's desire for adventure, I saddled up Smokey and headed for the hills. I knew where I was going – I planned to steal precious stones from the greedy dwarves. This was an important challenge for me; a test of stealth, courage and riding ability.

At first we walked to conserve energy, along a mountain track which led up from the old mine. I'd been told to stay away from this place as there was a tunnel that hadn't been safely filled in yet. I'd been told it could swallow both Smokey and me, and nobody would ever find us again as we'd fall through to the bowels of the earth. It was an eerie setting where dark things muttered and slithered under the brambles and nettles. Needless to say, I loved going there.

Some of the mine buildings still stood, defeated and lonesome, their empty doorways yawning desolate and black. I saw little flickers, eyes blinking in the darkness. It was the pit pony ghosts and the dead children who worked for the dark elves that lurked there. The railway track leading up from the village was gone and the few rusty mine carts left accepted their fate. Nature was a she dragon devouring the mine. I averted my eyes as we left and turned my attention to my quest. The dwarf castle loomed up ahead.

The entrance lay along a track lined with oak and hazel trees, their leaves copper and gold against a backdrop of cobalt blue sky. Most had begun to fall to earth, dead soldiers cast aside, forsaken by their masters. As we moved along the track my pulse quickened and adrenalin began to flow. I nudged Smokey into a gallop, reanimating the tiny corpses in a macabre death dance. The middle of the track was soft with mud and the sides were dry and stony. I kept to the middle so Smokey wouldn't hurt herself on a stone. The wet mulch muffled her hoof beats so I could keep galloping until I was on the other side of the stone-pillared entrance. Then I stopped and secretly turned back along the path. Now, I whispered to Smokey, we have to execute extreme stealth.

Pungent rotten wood and fungus emanated from the disturbed mud of the track revealing the black earth underneath, a scar slicing through the bronzed autumn skin. I leant forward quietly over Smokey's neck so my bobbing head would not be seen over the wall by the dwarf lords, and approached the gateway pillars. Holding my breath I stroked her to calm her, hoping she wouldn't startle in the face of danger. Then I rose up like a centaur. In front of me was a dwarf with a barrow of precious stones. His wrinkly face, half covered by a long white trailing beard, started in shock.

This dwarf wore the dark brown leather jerkin and green pointed hat of the earth workers. He wasn't a warrior, and apart from a dagger, I knew he was relatively harmless, but if I wasn't quick he would alert the dwarf lords before I could get my prize. His gravelly voice began to call out, alerting his fellow workers that a centaur was upon them. Smokey stamped her feet impatiently. I knew I had to move fast. Swiftly I reached my hand into the barrow and prised out three gems. Clutching them tightly I leant close to Smokey's neck again as we galloped back down the track, any minute expecting to hear the warrior's horn of pursuit.

On reaching the end of the track I slowed Smokey to a walk and chuckled. They believed I was a centaur. Proudly I sat up straight and looked back. The leaf corpses were quietly returning to their deathbeds, some already lost and sodden in the disturbed mud, and the house with the pillars was silent. Birds tweeted overhead preparing for the long winter months, whilst gangs of swallows gathered along a single telegraph wire gearing themselves up for their long journey south. They were all oblivious to my triumph.

The dwarves were not chasing us brandishing swords, but had turned to stone statues on the gateposts holding stone wheelbarrows discoloured and mottled with lichen. Inside the wheelbarrows there were no gems, but what looked like broken bits of coloured glass cemented together. But I knew better. Smokey was eager to head for home now, her breath white clouds in the crisp autumn air. I caressed her neck and opened my hand; there in my palm lay a ruby, an emerald and a deep blue sapphire. Smiling I placed them in my anorak pocket.

Life and Death

One day Smokey and I were out protecting the realm near a haunted house where a wicked ogre lived. It sat tall on a hill just like a house a child would draw, except this didn't have curtains, or flowers in the windows and a pretty picket fence. The windows were shattered and grey rags hung limp on the inside. Tall trees surrounded it, their branches gnarled and twisted like witches dancing. I heard the low warning croak of a raven and something else, something pitiful like the wail of a child.

At the side of the track, before the gate that led off the mountain into the village, lay a sheep. I got off Smokey and crept towards her. A tiny lamb sprang to its feet, head and legs wobbling like a puppet held up by strings. It cried out to me. At first I hung back thinking it had just been born; I didn't want the mother sheep to feel harassed into getting up to run away. Then I realised something was wrong. Flies buzzed around her back end, and this new-born seemed far too weak. It cried again before falling to its knees, and feebly butted the underside of the mother in a futile attempt to feed.

I lifted the reins over Smokey's head and looped them onto a fence post. Gently I approached the lamb, which appeared to have no fear of me. Then I saw the mother sheep's face. Her tongue was protruded and swollen. Her eyes had been taken by the crows that – as I glanced around – appeared to be gathering. A murder of crows is a fitting description. The lamb got to its feet and let out a woeful bleat and began to suck on my outstretched finger. I lifted it into my arms and there I held a life as dear as any.

An elderly woman approached, heading back from the village, and on seeing me said, "Take it home love; it was there when I walked down." She gestured down the path with her head, that was wrapped up tightly in a cream and green headscarf, then she gestured towards the haunted house. "He'll throw it to his dogs alive if you don't, you mark my words," and she trudged away without a backward glance. I looked towards the ogre's house and it loomed over us, the dark clouds creating a ghastly backdrop. I held the pathetic little life closer to my chest. A large crow flapped to the ground and I heard the ominous croak of the raven.

"Come along little one," I said to the lamb, "your mum can't help you now but Smokey and I can." I laid it gently over the front of my saddle and Smokey stood like a rock whilst I got on. It hung there limp and fragile like a dead rabbit, only its tiny bleats giving any clue that it was still alive. I stroked its little head as we rode up the main road, homeward bound. "I'm going to call you Lucky," I said. "Lucky the lamb."

Luckily for Lucky she must have helped herself to the rich colostrum milk as her mother died. This made sure she had all her antibodies and would survive as a bottle-fed lamb. She flourished. Friends from school came to visit, to have a go at bottle-feeding her. She was a feisty little thing and you had to hold the bottle tightly or she'd pull it from your hands. I taught her to walk on the lead, and even though she slept in the field, she spent a lot of time with the dog. She came for walks up the mountain, and when allowed off the lead she would run and bounce on all four legs in that crazy way sheep do, but she never went to join the other sheep. I'm sure she believed she was a dog – well if not, then certainly part of our family.

That last summer with Smokey was one of the happiest of my life. I was confident and my riding now excelled. I had horsey friends – Mari, Caryl and Donna – who had their own ponies and lived close by. Mari and I narrowly escaped the ogre's wrath whilst building jumps out of fallen wood. He'd yelled at us to get off his land and when I tried to apologise he said I'd have to speak up because he didn't have an ear. He proceeded to unwind filthy rags from around his head to show us. Well I turned and fled before realising Mari was holding both ponies and I had to run back to get Smokey and struggle to get on before we galloped away from whatever horrific sight awaited underneath the rags.

Another time whilst struggling to find our way across the moor because the boggarts had moved the tracks again, Donna and I rode straight into peat bogs. The ponies began to sink and stamped nervously, backtracking. Smokey was wise and I left her to find her way to safety. Donna's pony was called Sullivan, an honest genuine bay gelding whom she loved dearly. I remember her looking at me anxiously saying, "If Sullivan goes down in this bog then I'm going down with him." A vision of Donna wearing a sailor's hat with HMS Sullivan written on it bravely saluting as they sank into the peaty darkness flittered through my mind. Luckily our ponies knew what they were doing and carried their over-adventurous riders home in time for tea.

Then one day as the autumn winds ripped the last leaves from the trees and winter settled across the land, I returned home from school to find my mother acting strangely. I wanted to go out and see to Smokey, who had developed quite a bad cough recently and I'd not been able to ride her. The vet had said it was the result of mouldy hay and being stabled. She wasn't stabled with us and our hay was good, but he'd said the damage must have been done when she was younger, and now being an aged pony it was taking its toll on her. My mother kept making up silly excuses as to why I couldn't go out, and in the end she simply had to tell me.

"Smokey has died," she said. "It happened this morning not long after you left for school. The vet said it was a heart attack because the cough had weakened it."

"What? No... Not my Smokey?" I stammered. "It can't be true." The very thought that Smokey could die had never occurred to me. We'd had animals die before, but nothing had prepared me for this. I ran out to the field, but only Sunnyboy and Lucky lifted their heads and wandered towards the gate. They seemed to be looking at me expectantly as if they might see her too. "Where is she?" I asked my mother who had followed me out. I had no idea what happened to large animals when they die. My mum explained that a silver lorry had come to fetch her and two men had taken her body away to bury her. "You mean she'll have a grave?" I asked stupidly, because I knew my mother was saying the first thing that came into her mind. She didn't reply and I didn't ask again. Of course, she didn't have a grave.

I wish someone had taken some hair from her – a piece of

mane I could keep – but I had nothing. I tried to collect some dirty hair from the inside of her rug but this wasn't enough to make one of those beautiful braided horse pendant keepsakes. Nevertheless, I kept it safe, wrapped in some tissue and locked in a jewellery box under my bed. A photo of the two of us I kept stuck to the headboard, and all our rosettes we had won together hung on a string along the wall. My friend from school, Tracie, bought me a leather bracelet with Smokey's name scorched into it and Caryl said I could ride her old pony whenever I wanted, because she had a new one. This was all fine, but nothing changed the fact that Smokey my pony was dead, and as my body hit the extreme emotions of puberty something dark and heavy crept into my soul. That winter I lost myself in books and Tolkien's Middle Earth became my hiding place.

Hell

I'll never forget Tessa's face when we arrived at Nice.

"Look Mummy, there are palm trees outside." I smiled at her as I approached the passport control and handed over our passports. It had been a long time since I'd even contemplated visiting France again, or even going abroad for that matter. Stepping off the plane I could feel the heat in the air and my perfume still lingered headily on my skin. I used to wear it when I lived here and felt the familiarity as amber and orange flower mingled with the heat, re-energising me.

The last time I had wandered through the cluttered streets of the old town in Nice, I'd been pregnant with Tessa – not uncomfortably so, for I'd had a relatively easy pregnancy. I recalled walking down a particularly beautiful street and sighing dreamily as I'd noticed a wall covered with dark pink bougain-villea flowers. At the end of the street, hidden between two tall, elegant saffron coloured buildings with bright white shutters framing black wrought iron Juliette balconies, sat a tall skinny house. It was an old-fashioned pink colour, like plaster. The shutters were old and the paint was cracked and chipped. On the ground floor was a traditional toyshop. I'd gone inside and seen a row of plain music boxes ready for painting. I had turned the handle of the nearest and '*The Sound of Silence*' filled the air.

I thought how I would miss this place if I returned home to damp soggy Wales.

An image of myself as a child with Smokey appeared in my mind. My father had taken me to Banwen pony club show. The dark, wet coal tip background swam through the Nice sunshine. I re-membered my father's proud, competitive face as he stated that he had entered me into the musical mug race. We, the compet-itors, just scruffy kids on scruffier ponies, their legs blackened from coal dust, had to circle a group of posts and when the music stopped, gallop as fast as we could to the posts with enamel mugs on top. We had to each grab a mug, and the rider left without one was knocked out; this continued until it was a race between two for the last mug standing.

My nerves were heightened as Smokey knew this game, and loved it. A steady drizzle fell, wetting the reins, and I could feel my hands sliding on the leather. Smokey's ears were pricked and when the tuneless melody stopped she darted, the first one across the field towards the mugs. Time stopped, and I could hear my own breath coming in gasps. I struggled to hold the reins in one hand as gingerly I let go with the other to lean out to snatch a mug as we whizzed past – and I missed. On circling back, I saw all the other riders pick off the remaining mugs, leaving me without. *You bloomin' sledge!* echoed my father's voice. *Smokey was the fastest there! All you had to do was grab a mug!* I smiled as the image faded.

A terse cough from the passport officer disturbed my reverie. His eyes were glancing rapidly from my passport to his computer screen and back to me, and then Tessa. I think I said something stupid like, "My photo isn't that bad is it?" and I laughed, hoping he would too and then hand me our passports and we could join the rest of the holiday makers on their way to the baggage carousel. However, there was a problem. I was escorted by armed police into a side room. There I learned in broken English that I was going to jail.

Tessa went from excited to terrified in the space of a few seconds. I thought there must be some mistake. I hadn't done anything. I quickly sent a few texts home to let them know there was a problem. My friend Tracie called me back. I told her I wasn't sure what was happening but to contact the British embassy in France and try to find out. Susan, who was waiting at arrivals, was brought to the office. She was as confused as I was but reassured me this was obviously a huge mistake. The police were talking rapidly on the phone and glancing at me. Susan could understand French and quickly took Tessa's passport and protectively put an arm around her shoulders as there was talk of contacting French social services.

I was asked to hand over my possessions. I wanted to keep my phone and wanted to speak with somebody from the embassy. I wasn't allowed. I was going to spend my first night back in France in a cell. I began to panic. Tessa fell to her knees in front of the policemen, placed her hands in prayer position and begged them to not take me away. She was crying, the policemen appeared uncomfortable and I'm certain they thought something wasn't quite right. I realised I had to make everything seem just one big mistake for Tessa's sake even though I had never been more frightened in my life.

I tried reassuring Tessa that I'd be with her soon and that she must start our holiday without me for now and be a good girl for Susan. She hugged me fiercely, tears smearing her cheeks before they took me to my cell. A cold band of fear clenched around my heart. Susan told me she would contact the embassy and my family and friends. She would stay in a hotel close to the airport and return in the morning when hopefully I would be released and this would all be a big misunderstanding.

I allowed myself, stripped of my possessions, wearing my new holiday dress and shoes, to be led to the awaiting cell. I sat mortified and confused. It hadn't registered properly. This was such an unlikely thing to happen to me that my brain was struggling to keep up. I was a mother and my little girl needed me.

I thought about when I left home for the first time at sixteen. I'd felt fear then. Fear of the unfamiliar. Fear of being alone. Fear of the dark. I remembered lying in my single bed in a stranger's house, dreading the morning when I would start my first day at work. I was too afraid to pee in case the family I lived with heard it. I was shy and timid, and moving from a place of comfort into an unknown environment is never easy. Humans don't like change. Little did I know that the road I was following would someday lead here.

Leaving home

My Mum had found a work placement for me about half an hour's car drive away. I had to live with another family and work on their hunting and jumping yard. I wasn't a hunt supporter and didn't hunt but it was only a small yard and I never went with them. My friends were sad and confused when I left, especially Tracie.

"They can't send you away to live with strangers," she said, shocked when I told her.

"I want to be a famous show jumper though," I'd answered, knowing deep down this was nonsense. "I need to take some horsey exams and I'm going to qualify as a riding instructor so I can have my own yard," I'd say confidently, although not feeling confident. I knew my parents didn't own enough land to set up a riding centre; how I thought I'd be able to do this I don't know. Tracie looked at me sadly, she didn't understand why I had to go away and to be honest neither did I. It all seemed so rushed. So, I left school with a handful of 'O'levels and after a few brief blissfully happy summer weeks I left home too.

The family I moved in with were lovely. Sylvia ran the horse yard and her husband worked away, coming home on weekends. They had two young children, a boy and a girl; both were nice kids. There was another girl starting the same time as myself but arriving the following day; she was a couple of years older. I was terrified that first lonely night. With my few measly possessions I sat on a pine framed single bed in a bare room which I would share with the other girl. I was too scared to go downstairs to sit with the family. I missed my friends and needed time to cry. Through my muffled sobbing I thought I heard wolves, their cries soft in the darkness drawing closer. Immediately I put them out of my mind, but secretly welcomed them as part of the magic of my childhood. I got into bed and began to read *The Lord of the Rings* – again.

The other girl was just as freaked out as me. We got on well and became friends. Another chap moved in to work too and there was a young girl and an annoying boy who kept their horses at the yard. I settled in and a good camaraderie was formed between us, the family and the livery clients. Even the farrier who would spend the whole day at the yard to shoe the horses became a good friend and still is. Although I missed my own friends terribly, I managed to fit in.

I now had another horse too. Frostie was a magnificent, and slightly crazy, 16hh three quarter thoroughbred crossed with a Welsh cob. He was only four years old and loved to jump. Soon, with my hair and his mane streaming in the wind, I was racing around Paxton's Tower, a Neo-Gothic folly overlooking the River Towy as it threaded through the patchwork land to Dinefwr castle in the distance. I'd found some magic once more.

Goodbye Frosted Dreams

It had been about two years since I'd lived at home. I'd passed all my horsey exams with distinction. I had grown up, felt exhausted and was desperately confused about my future. Wherever my dreams of horses took me, the big money beast shambled behind brandishing its net ready to snare me and drag me back down to earth. I wasn't going to be a show jumper and I wasn't going to be able to afford to set up my own yard. I became depressed and began to give up on my future, becoming careless and slovenly. The only blessing was being back amongst my friends. I started to go to rock festivals, partying until late and freeing my rebellious soul, a side of myself I had never met before. I was losing myself and my direction.

I was lucky to still have Frostie, and often took to the hills in search of that magical feeling. I spent most days galloping about with my sister, Caryl and Donna. Sunnyboy was still alive and going strong. On the weekends, and most nights, I would go out with friends. I passed my driving test and bought a cheap car with my dad's help. I'd need transport for work, but there wasn't much around locally for a riding instructor and I wasn't ready to leave home again.

Unemployment didn't go down well with my mother; it embarrassed her. She drove me to a local factory and shoved me inside to get a job. Within a month I was made redundant. I was unable to talk to her about why she wanted me to work in a factory when I had spent ages working at my horse exams. Couldn't she just give me some time to breathe? I should have used my head and gone to college or university, got my life back on track. I was young enough, not yet twenty. Then one day, having just walked out of a job stacking shelves in a supermarket, I saw a job advertised in the job centre window. It was at a horse and pony Trust and Rescue Centre. I called the number, went for an interview and got the job.

The job was a twenty-five-mile drive there and back five days a week. It was hard going but I loved it. The founder of the Trust was a trooper for horse and animal rescue. She taught me about the wild Welsh ponies: how a wild horse is different to a domesticated horse, how they think and how to interact with them and gain their trust. It was through her and the ponies I began to rediscover myself. I was beginning to feel excited about life again.

My confidence was growing and so was my self-esteem. I took treks out with school kids in tow all clutching desperately to chunks of mane. Ponies are so delightfully funny yet brave, strong and gentle all at once. They helped me rediscover the spirit of the horse. This had nothing to do with competition and my shallow obsession with wanting to be a show jumper. This was learning a new way of communicating with these deeply magical beasts. In the eyes of a small wild colt I saw more spirit and energy than I'd ever seen in any domesticated show horse.

Soon I developed a craving for adventure that could not be sated locally. I wanted more experience with different horses. The wild ponies had taught me there was much more to the horse than show jumping, so I thanked them for their wisdom and moved on. After a stint at an Arabian showing yard, where I learnt to look after show stallions, I applied for a job at an endurance competition yard in Exmoor, Somerset. I was invited for an interview, met the horses and my new boss, and got the job.

Taking the job meant travelling away from home again. I was nervous and frightened but also excited to be going somewhere new. I was realising my whole life lay ahead of me. Since I'd abandoned my desire to show jump a whole new horsey world was opening up. I wanted to get a good job and see different places and use the qualifications I'd worked so hard to get. There was a lot more I could do, show jumping was not the be all and end all. The new job paid more than I had ever received before. There was just one big spanner in the works: Frostie couldn't come with me.

After many tears I decided to put my beloved horse out on loan with a view to sell. The family that took him loved him and decided to go forward with the purchase. I tried not to think of Frostie leaving, although it was constantly on my mind when I drove to Exmoor. I hummed along to the melodic notes of Peter Gabriel's *Salisbury Hill* as I passed over the Severn bridge and headed south, away from Wales. It was a cloudy, murky day which reflected my befuddled thoughts. Had I done the right thing? I worried about what would happen to him when he got old. Surely the family would take care of him. They were rich people; they'd give him the life he deserved. I needed to concentrate on my new job and forget about Frostie, he would be much better off without me. I pushed it to the back of my mind and concentrated on my new beginnings.

The Evil Host Rides

The endurance yard was beautiful, my boss lived in what can only be described as a small manor house and my accommodation was the lodge house. Now I really had a chance to get into competition – endurance competition that is, and I relished it. The moorlands were wild and rugged yet soft and spongy under foot, making it some of the best riding country ever. I would tear across the moor on a little Arabian horse, chestnut tail held high like a flag, pulling at the bit whilst a herd of deer galloped alongside. Then quick as a flash, they would change direction, leaving us to reach the cairn atop the hill alone and watch them disappear over the far ridge. Despite being a magical place of exquisite natural beauty Exmoor had an evil side, a dark host that I was about to discover, and I would realise I could not live there anymore. Underneath the picture postcard front festered a nasty, barbaric heart.

I was a member of the League Against Cruel Sports, which had a base in Exmoor near Dulverton. This immediately made me an enemy in the hunting-obsessed village of Exford. This was before the ban on hunting with dogs. Having not really seen any large hunts, only the local Welsh hunts which I hated, I was completely unprepared for what was to come when hunting season began. At first it was just unfriendly looks when I parked my car in the village. My anti-blood sport car sticker I'd had as part of my welcome pack from the League had been spotted. The local pub resembled a mortuary for wildlife. I was shocked to see the amount of stag heads, fox heads and even legs and paws stuffed and mounted on the walls.

I thought I could turn a blind eye; my boss didn't hunt, she was above such things. In fact she'd had an argument with the local hunt regarding one of her Arab horses becoming injured due to the hunt illegally passing over her land. Nevertheless, encounter their unpleasantness I did. I'd found a nail in my tyre one day; nothing suspicious about that, but it kept on happening until I had two nails in two tyres. Then I had my wheel nuts loosened and I could have crashed or even been killed; luckily a friend spotted it before any harm was done.

The worst was when I went to visit friends for a weekend and my boss was left to feed my cat, which she would gladly do. When I returned she was quite distressed and informed me my cat had died. She explained she had been run over and the gardener had found her body and buried her before I came home. I was devastated. Maddy didn't go out on the lane, it was a long way from the house and she didn't wander far. I had a prickly sensation like someone was stalking quietly over my grave. It was a sense, a warning. I was not welcome. My boss had her own circle of friends and didn't bother with the locals, she was rich and respected so they left her alone but even she, I believe, was too afraid to stand up to the hunt bullies.

One cold autumn day I saw a stag. He ran, steaming and puffing, soaked in sweat, onto the yard. We had an open ended internal stable yard. His silhouette was outlined in the archway, the trees and hedges a backdrop of copper in the sun. His eyes met mine and I froze, willing him to enter so I could go around the outside and close the gate so he could be safe. Maybe I could save him from a terrifying and pitiful death at the hands of the bloodthirsty bullies. He was only there for seconds but I felt him. His ancient wisdom hovered in the air with a musky scent of earth. Time stopped as his flanks heaved. He exhaled. Puffs of breath mingled with the rising steam from his sweat darkened flanks, his coat thick and rugged.

The high-pitched piercing call of the hunting horn echoed from across the fields and the spell was broken. He sprang away towards the valley. I dropped the buckets I had been carrying and ran outside calling him, begging him to trust me to come back. I'd give him hay and not let them get him. The evil host came into view. That damned horn merged with the braying hounds – the sound of fear and death. Over the hill they streamed. First the red coats, then the black, the lithe hound bodies filling the spaces between the riders like liquid. After him they went and somewhere in that valley I heard the death cry. He had lost.

It was approaching Christmas and I had arranged for my girl-friends from Wales to come and visit. I'd heard of a local charity dance happening in the village hall. They encouraged me to go and with their company I felt confident. I had a couple of friends in the village, one of the pubs wasn't so hunt obsessed and I knew the cook; he liked rock music and had long hair. We dressed up and wrapped up then walked down to the village and into the lounge of the cosy little pub. My friend popped out of the kitchen to say hi and I introduced him to the girls.

We enjoyed a few drinks and laughs before heading to the village hall, avoiding the animal mortuary pub popular with the hunt. When we entered I saw a couple of unfriendly faces. These were not the huntsmen themselves, they were too haughty to go to the local village hall, but a breed called the hunt follower – sad, nasty people that follow the hunt with Land Rovers simply to get off on the kill. There was a raffle with one of the prizes being a pig's head. We didn't buy any raffle tickets but proceed-ed to enjoy a couple of drinks and play pool. I noticed one of the men staring at us and as he got drunker he began to parade around with the pig's head on his own head, snorting. He and his friends danced whilst the pig's eyes stared, empty and dead.

The girls and I decided to leave. As we reached the doorway the pig's head man came after us.

"That's right, clear off, you anti-hunt bitches," he sneered.

"Back off," I told him, feeling not only my temper rising, but also fear.

He kept coming, letting the insults flow freely. I was behind Elaine, one of my friends, and he pushed me. I went sprawling. I tried to get up but he sprang at me, pulling my hair and hitting my face. Then I could feel someone kicking me and I heard a woman's voice yell,

"Gerroff my husband you bitch!"

Elaine tried to stop them and pulled me up whilst my other friends yelled at them to leave me alone. All four of us staggered out of there to an onslaught of insults and threats from grown men.

We called the police when we got back to my house, and a

policeman who introduced himself as PC Donny Osmond turned up. This made it all the more surreal and for a moment I thought it was the hunt pulling a frightening joke on me. In fact that was his name and the only advice he could give me was not to press charges.

"With all this freezing weather," he droned in his local accent, "they've not been able to hunt so all that frustration has to come out somehow and it'll take a brave person to stand up to the hunt in Exford."

For a few weeks after this, I was afraid to go to bed, afraid of what stunts they would pull next. A police car from Taunton drove by a couple of times in the evenings which didn't really make me feel any safer. At night I would hear the poor hounds in the hunt kennels howling like lost souls – or was it the fear wolves outside my door? I hoped the ban on hunting with dogs would soon be passed but it was not coming soon enough for me, and it would take years to change such a narrow-minded cruel mentality. That's when I knew my time on Exmoor had come to an end. I was ready for another adventure, another quest; the world was my oyster. I was young, confident and determined to make the best of my life. My talent with horses could take me anywhere I wanted to go. I just needed to decide where. I'd always wanted to work with the majestic horses of Iberia, the Royal Horse of Europe. So I set about finding myself another job.

Hell

I wondered how long I'd be held before they realised I was innocent. A woman police officer told me it could be six months before they would look at my case. Then maybe I could go home,
if what I said was true. I'd already been tried and found guilty
because I had not turned up to my own trial, a trial I'd known
nothing about.

I'd come on holiday. What sort of idiot knowingly comes on
holiday with her daughter to a country where she knows she is a
wanted criminal? Why couldn't they see this was a stupid thing
to do and if I was what they thought I was then surely I wouldn't
be so stupid? I was clueless to what my crime was, which only
added to my fear. Was I even in the real world anymore or had
I slipped into the pages of a book, a story about some other
unfortunate?

There were loud noises, huge bangs which sounded like
explosions, that echoed down the corridors. Had I slipped into
some alternate war-torn reality? Were the police under attack?
Not long ago there had been a terrorist strike on Nice. Did they
think I was a terrorist? I closed my eyes to the torrent of
questions and hoped I was dreaming and asleep on the plane.
What book had I been reading? It was a thriller. Yes. I must be
dreaming and any minute the pilot would announce we were
about to land, and I would wake up and see Tessa's smiling
face... But there was no announcement.

I had a pain in my jaw. There was a small lump. I'd had it
tested and it was benign. I used to clench my jaw at night
causing terrible pain. I'd been doing this for years. Now I was
obviously clenching it again and it was starting to throb. I called
out a few times and a kind looking policeman arrived. I asked
him for painkillers but he didn't know what I said. He told me
to wait and returned with a woman police officer. I explained to
her about my jaw. I told her about the lump and pointed to it
but she backed away from me, a look of disgust in her eyes.
What did she think I was? She translated to the man and they
both left. He returned alone and handed me a plastic cup of

water with two tablets. "Why is it so noisy?" I asked. "What are those bangs?" He just shrugged as if he didn't understand and walked away.

If I was a bad person and had committed a serious offence then very well, fair enough I'd been busted and that was that. I would understand why they looked at me the way they did and more importantly I'd know what I was in a cell for. I'd also be a certain type of person. I'd be hard, have thicker skin and be able to cope – but I wasn't that person. Things like this didn't happen to people like me. I was not prepared. I'd never even had a parking ticket. I was unfamiliar with crime and prison. Both my parents had been law-abiding people and I'd been brought up that way. Apart from smoking a bit of pot I'd never intentionally done anything illegal. I thought about how as a young adult I'd always wanted to travel and find adventure. Why wasn't I satisfied with what I had? This was one adventure I wanted no part of.

I stood up and called out, "Please, help me! I'm innocent! I don't even know what I've done." My words clattered awkwardly down an empty corridor. They were fed up of my pleading; I suppose everyone they ever locked up claimed to be innocent. But I really was.

Adventures in a Portuguese Wonderland: The Fool's Journey

I had arrived at Faro airport in the Algarve feeling rather dazed. What had I done? Had I gone mad? I remembered my friend Neil as he waved me off at Gatwick saying, "Have a good one!" meaning a good life experience I suppose. Why my parents hadn't dropped me off I didn't know. I didn't question it at the time although I look back and it does make me wonder. I can't quite remember even saying goodbye to them. I suppose I was used to not living at home, but moving abroad to foreign shores was quite a big step and with no social media sites, and mobile phones still a thing of the future, it gave me the impression of being further away and more remote than I actually was.

I followed the stream of people heading towards the baggage carousel and after a momentary feeling of pure dread that my rucksack may not have made it, I relaxed as it eventually jiggered towards me along the conveyor belt. I hoisted it up onto my back and banished the negative thoughts that kept springing into my head like exploding geysers. This was the start of my adventure and I was going to enjoy it no matter what. I was a fully qualified riding instructor and horse trainer and had been riding since I was a child. I was on a quest to discover more about the beautiful, majestic horses of the Iberian Peninsula. This was my adventure.

I was scheduled to meet Nancy at the 'Meeting Point' at the airport. I had no idea what a 'Meeting Point' looked like, or Nancy for that matter. I was just about to attempt to ask someone where it was, when I saw it up ahead. I couldn't miss it: a large sign with the words 'Meeting Point' in English hung above a few chairs. I hastened towards them and sat down staring expectantly at every woman that walked past on the off chance it may be Nancy. After ten minutes a woman hurried towards me. She was about thirty years old with fair hair and skin that had been tanned and freckled by the Portuguese sun. She was wearing shorts and a T-shirt and looked like she was about to embark on a scout and guide jamboree.

"Hi, I'm so sorry I'm late, I had a load of guests to drop off at departures and the traffic has been awful," she explained. "I'm Nancy, pleased to meet you." She held out her hand which I shook. I could tell by her accent and fair, sun freckled skin that she was Irish, like my new boss Richard. I smiled and introduced myself, feeling relieved to have met the person I was meant to have met. She too seemed relieved that I was the right person and herded me off in the direction of the car park. As I stepped outside of the air-conditioned airport, the heat thumped me in the chest and I breathed my first lungful of Portuguese air.

"Oh God it's hot!" I exclaimed, quite shocked as my Welsh body, that had just been living on Exmoor, tried to adjust itself. Usually I was in the habit of feeling cold and drizzle whenever I stepped outside.

"Yes," said Nancy, "it's been unusually hot this spring, although it's a little cooler on the Alentejo coast where we're based," she added, as we headed towards a white Toyota people carrier. "The Portuguese roads and drivers are something else you're going to have to get used to too, they're terrible!"

Just how terrible they actually were, I experienced immediately, as we joined the highway and began the two-and-a-half hour drive to my new home. The hard shoulder, I discovered was not for breakdowns, but where a slower driver would be pushed, so three cars could travel abreast if there were only two available lanes. If you didn't abide by this rule they would either toot until you got out of the way or overtake you on the inside, therefore using the hard shoulder as the fast lane. This, combined with being in a left hand drive vehicle on the wrong side of the road to which I was accustomed, was quite disconcerting.

Eventually we arrived at Villa Nova de Milfontes, the local town. Nancy drove down the main street towards the little fishing port. It was beautiful. Narrow streets lined with cafés, bars and restaurants beckoned invitingly. Tourist shops, their wares spilling outside the doors, bedazzled as the sun reflected upon glazed and painted terracotta bowls and jugs piled high on the streets. I blinked, almost blinded by the small white houses that sprawled lazily, their windows and doors bordered in yellow or blue and capped with rustic, red brown roofs. Orange trees with bright, shiny leaves decorated every garden where scarlet geraniums gazed like exotic harlots and white jasmine peeped shyly from shaded terraces. Everything was so colourful in contrast to the grey, drizzle-smothered country I had left behind.

Milfontes is an estuary town, which sits on the north side of the River Mira where it joins the Atlantic Ocean about halfway between Lisbon and the Algarve. A few small fishing boats were moored in the harbour, overlooked by a quaint restaurant.

"That restaurant does the most amazing garlic tiger prawns," Nancy said. "We take the guests there for their last evening meal, as a treat."

"I'm vegetarian, so I don't eat meat or fish," I replied. "Although I've been thinking I may begin to eat fish whilst here." Nancy looked at me in shock and then what may have been pity.

"You'll have to start eating some meat or fish soon then, because vegetarian food is pretty impossible to find," she said rather dubiously.

I agreed to consider this as I noticed an old man in the harbour. Thick grey hair framed a wrinkled brown face. He leapt out of a small boat carrying a freshly caught octopus in a bucket. Smiling triumphantly, he headed towards the restaurant. I watched horrified as tentacles reached out over the rim of the bucket gesturing to me for help. Shamefully I averted my eyes.

As the river reached the turquoise sea, waves lapped gently over the soft white sand. The beach was a paradise of dreamy deserted coves. It was a hidden gem, completely unspoilt by mass development. Right on the beach, resting on a broad wooden deck, was a café with a red awning offering welcome shade from the sun. A couple of young lads with their girlfriends relaxed at the tables, barefoot in swimming costumes, drinking beer. I regarded them enviously, thinking that could be me soon.

"Do you surf?" asked Nancy.

"Not really," I said. "I've had a go messing around on the Gower peninsula, although the weather doesn't do much to entice you into the water in Wales."

"Richard and I surf, whenever we get a chance," she said smiling to herself. "There is a fantastic beach we go to just along the coast at Praia do Malhao. The surf is amazing due to the massive swells from the Atlantic." I pictured her and my new boss confidently surfing the Atlantic swells of this breath-taking coastline. The surrounding countryside was wild and untouched. Miles of sandy tracks wound through cork oak forests before breaking free onto open plains dotted with brightly coloured pink and yellow succulents. There was an abundance of wildlife and an array of protected birdlife, including the huge elegant storks that build their nests precariously on the cliff tops nearby. I was immediately in love and awe of this wonderful place.

The trail riding centre where I would live and work was about a fifteen minute drive into the hills. The lane wound down into a glorious river valley and crossed a green meadow dotted with large yellow and purple irises. A delightful looking cottage, lime-washed white with traditional yellow borders, lounged above the meadow, the old terracotta tiled roof hanging low over the windows. Between two cork trees hung a large washing line full of bed sheets swaying in the warm, late afternoon breeze. I gazed at what seemed to me a picture of pure bliss and idyllic tranquillity. Later my illusions were shattered when I discovered it was the local brothel, which certainly explained the amount of sheets that were regularly on the line.

We turned off a tarmac lane and onto a sandy track that led down to my new home. There were no other houses in sight and the track just got rougher. Nancy explained it was the horrendous amount of rainfall during the rainy season that had damaged it so badly. I looked at the deep ravines and potholes and wondered just how heavy the rain fell in this blissful place of sunshine. Rounding a bend and crossing a small stream I noticed century cactuses, their triffid like flowering stalks mournfully reaching to the sky. Then a large white building with a terracotta roof that housed the stalls for the horses came into view.

"The horses come in to be tethered, a rope either side of their head collars to eat, be groomed and prepared for the trails, placing their heads between gaps in the bars much like cattle stalls," explained Nancy, as I eyed the building.

"I can't wait to meet them," I told Nancy excitedly.

"Oh, they've already been fed now and turned back out," she said. "You'll get to meet them properly tomorrow." I stared into the dry, dusty, arid fields where I could see mainly grey and white horses with some dark bays and chestnuts gathered around various large galvanised mangers munching on straw, as hay was impossible to come by.

The next building was of similar style and referred to as the clubhouse. It was just a large open plan room with white walls and a terracotta tiled floor with a kitchen containing a gas cooker and fridge. It was powered by a generator which was hardly ever on as it drank fuel and was extremely noisy, so the fridge became a glorified and smelly cupboard. I learnt never to eat the mayonnaise that happened to be left in there. The clubhouse also housed toilets and a shower which needed the generator in order to pump the water that came from the well. On the outside everything looked delightful until I remember attempting my first shower where I innocently waited for water only to be blinded by liquid mud spurting over me. In shock I reeled and panicked as the thick brown sludge bubbled through the shower head, blocking it. I unscrewed the end and waited as the mud subsided to be replaced by brown water which was as good as I was going to get.

We drove around the back of this building and I eagerly looked for the self-contained apartment I had been promised. Nancy however, parked next to an old fashioned, tear-drop caravan. Not a large comfortable static, but a very small touring one. The little door was open and on the table was a single candle. The other table had been dropped into a bed position. There was no toilet, shower, electricity or even a working gas cooker, although there was a bottle of mineral water.

"This is where you'll be staying," said Nancy. "It's only temporary until Debbie moves out of your room."

"Who's Debbie?" was all I could bring myself to say.

"Oh, she is the girl who you'll be replacing; she's moving on now. I'll pick you up in an hour to go to the restaurant and meet everyone." And with that she hurried away before I could even comment. It was a good job I'd brought a sleeping bag and travel pillow which I thought I'd need only for the trails. I surveyed my tiny abode and sat down exhausted, only to burst into tears. Nobody ran to my aid so crying was a pretty pointless waste of energy. Drying my eyes, I decided to embrace my adventure and looked around.

It was peaceful and beautiful. The countryside was unique to that area and so different to what I was used to. Sandy tracks stretched through eucalyptus trees into the mountains whilst ancient twisted cork oaks rested on the sandy plains. Their trunks were two-toned in various stages of red brown to dark brown. They had a number painted in white on the lighter parts which depicted the year their cork had been harvested. There was a sweet aroma in the air that came from the sticky gum cistus plants and their delicate cream flowers that grew everywhere.

I approached the horse paddocks and the contented horsey sounds eased my feelings of desolation. I noticed a tall pale chestnut mare with zebra markings on her hind legs and a broad dorsal stripe down her back. Although too tall to be a purebred she reminded me of the rare Sorraia ponies that are found only in Portugal that have these primitive markings. A noble looking, almost Roman-nosed, dapple grey horse with an arched neck and long mane stopped eating and returned my gaze across the field. There was no mistaking the look of a Lusitano there. The legendary battle horse and royal horse of Europe stared back at me across the arid ground.

Feeling inspired, I returned to the tiny caravan and unpacked my rucksack. My riding boots and leather Australian hat took pride of place. After squashing my clothes into the tiny wardrobe I laid out my sleeping bag. This was my adventure and I couldn't wait to get started. I lay on the bed to wait for Nancy but had to get up to chase the flies, that insisted on crawling over every inch of my face, out of the door. I soon learnt that roasting inside the caravan with the doors and windows closed, was preferable to being eaten alive by flies.

A Choking Meeting

The white Toyota people carrier pulled up outside and I climbed into the passenger seat. I was starving and Nancy seemed to prattle on about everything and anything, I think in an attempt to avoid the fact that my living conditions were far from acceptable. I was just relieved to be heading to the local restaurant as I was starving. We pulled up outside a typical basic Portuguese café/restaurant just off the main road, not a tourist affair. We passed through the café part and into the restaurant beyond. It was like stepping into a brightly lit school canteen. The tables had plastic wipe clean tablecloths covered in disposable white tissue arranged lengthways with plastic chairs.

There, engulfing the table with his presence, was my larger than life boss Richard. He was in his mid-thirties, very tall and good looking in a charming cheeky way. Instantly I felt a strange vibe emanate from Nancy and realised that she may be in love with him, even if she didn't quite realise it and he in turn didn't even notice her existence. He was married and doted upon his wife Sheena. She was older than him and looked to have been very beautiful and this still shone through a 'lived in' visage. She was a horse mistress of classical equitation and had trained with some of the greats. I was eager to learn from her.

Richard dominated all conversation, his loud Irish vocals filling the room. He called for the Portuguese waiters and ordered me a Sagres beer. He gesticulated with his arms in a 'welcome to all I survey' gesture, as if he was the lord and master and everyone else were mere peasants. I found myself saying how satisfied I was with my accommodation, and to not worry as it was fine and I realised only temporary. He had such a beguiling charm that it was impossible to voice any kind of complaint towards him. I felt like I'd arrived at the Mad Hatter's tea party. Sheena on the other hand seemed impenetrable to this charm, as if she abided on a different planet.

With no alternative available I agreed to the fish dish that was on the menu for the evening. Debbie, my predecessor, had not yet arrived and I was halfway through my beer when the door opened and she walked quietly in, carrying a bike helmet and wearing a biker's leather jacket. Richard stood up and boomed,

"Debbie! How fantastic you could make it!" He rushed over and gave her a hug. She looked at him as if he were insane.

"Meet our new guide," he said. "Your replacement." Then he hurriedly added, "Not that we could ever replace you, but she's a riding instructor from Wales."

Debbie scowled a smile and took her place opposite. I smiled back at her and hoped she didn't think me a posh jumped-up riding instructor, as in reality I was a confused young girl who'd come looking for adventure and was now not really sure why. She ordered a beer and asked me where in Wales I was from. I informed her it was Swansea and discovered she was from Bristol. We spoke about horses and soon realised we had relatively identical horsey backgrounds. Conversation all around was awkward as I was feeling rather intimidated by these strangers surrounding me and I was relieved when the food arrived.

The fish smelled beautiful, cod smothered in oil and garlic. In my hunger and inexperience at eating fish I choked on a fish bone. It was not even a small bone but a great big chunk. I felt it in my mouth just before it slid down my oesophagus and lodged there. I began to cough and splutter, struggling to breathe; my eyes were watering as I indicated to my throat. Sheena realised I may have a bone stuck and gave me some bread to eat as she said this would catch it and make it easier to swallow. I ate some bread which also lodged against the bone, restricting my breathing even more. I could not speak and in my fear that I was about to vomit over the table I ran to the toilets with Debbie and Sheena following carrying more bread.

I tipped my head over the toilet bowl and coughed and strained and could feel my throat contract into vomit mode when Debbie slapped me on the back and the offending bone flew into the toilet bowl with a load of chewed up bread and vomit.

"That's a bloody vertebra!" she exclaimed looking down the toilet. "Bread wouldn't have shifted that."

"Oh my goodness," said Sheena. "It must have been a very large cod."

By the end of the night I was well and truly exhausted and quite frankly would have slept on a clothesline. The thought of my tiny caravan didn't seem so bad after all – although nothing seemed bad after a large glass of Portuguese brandy. Debbie had to rush off but would be back later. I asked if I could see her bike first and she proudly showed me her beautiful classic Triumph Tiger 750cc in midnight blue. She explained that she had ridden it over from England on her own. I liked this girl, she was my kind of person.

Back at my caravan I realised I had no matches or lighter to light my candle. I had never smoked much either so didn't habitually carry a lighter. I lay in the darkness listening to the strange, alien night-time sounds which I would begin to know and love. Sleep was about to claim me when I heard Debbie's motorbike returning. She smoked, she would have matches. I grabbed my Maglite and opened the caravan door.

We lit my candle and I invited Debbie in for a chat; she had a small battery powered CD player and I had brought a few of my favourite CDs. I got to learn and understand a little bit more of where I had come to and what to expect. She told me about the horses and of her plans for the future, her wish to become a self-employed horse trainer. She gave me hope. I would work at the trail centre, and not get upset about my accommodation. This was an adventure after all. Debbie's little room wasn't much better than the caravan but it wasn't so bad; I would spend most of the time out on the trails. I could move out in time and maybe get my own place. Whilst dreaming of our futures and smoking Portuguese cigarettes – to the haunting melodies of Fairport Convention – Debbie and I forged our lifelong friendship.

My Painted Scrap of Skin

It was in this wonderland that I found my best friend in horse terms too: Wynnie. Debbie and I met some Germans who had horses, including two new-born foals. They invited us over to see them. As soon as we got there it was easy to tell that these people were simply stoned hippies trying to live off the land but too out of it to have much success. Portugal at this time was full of these lost wanderers. Dreamy eyed stone heads seeking an escape from reality only to return to Mummy and Daddy with their tails between their legs many years later, trying desperately to rejoin the normal world, hoping it wasn't too late. The farm they lived in was barren and badly situated in a dried-up dustbowl. The scary thing was, they had a baby too.

There were two very skinny mares eating dried carob pods. Their foals hid behind them, heads hanging near their mother's tails in a bid to keep the flies from their eyes. One mare in particular was very thin and weak. She was a dull black with a broken down back, like she had carried too much weight in her short life. She was only eight years old. Her foal stepped out from behind her, his proud face held aloft. *Was this a threat?* I could feel him think. I walked cautiously through the dusty ground feeling the heat burning down on my head, my eyes crinkling in the sun.

Sitting down on my haunches I waited for them to come to me, my hand outstretched. The dull black mare edged closer but seemed disinterested, not smelling any available food in my hand, but her foal was far more inquisitive. My heart missed a beat as he boldly stretched his nose to brush against my fingers before skittering away and staring at me. Then deeming me safe and not a threat he approached again; his mother seemed unconcerned, continuing to nibble at the carob pods.

His dark brown coat had large white patches like someone had spilt paint on him. He had white legs but his head and neck remained dark as old oak. His grandfather apparently had been a wild mustang destined for the European slaughter houses and had been bought by Gypsies. His father belonged to Gypsies too, out of a Lusitano mare. He had been wandering loose and covered the German couple's mares when the Gypsies had passed through the area.

His foal mane was straggly and stuck up like a mohawk. He looked at me with wild mustang eyes. Even though he was small and weedy, just a painted scrap of skin, he had such a powerful presence. I had to save him from this desolate place and these dim-witted hippies that clearly hadn't a clue how to look after horses. Coloured horses were quite rare in Portugal at this time, and I remembered my boss at the wild pony rescue in Wales telling me that coloured horses had the bravest spirits.

He held my eye and cautiously stepped towards me to sniff my hand. In my crouched position I held my face towards his inquisitive nostrils and calmed my breath like the wild ponies had taught me. He inhaled my scent and relaxed. I blew slowly into his nose and began to scratch his neck. He leaned into me, utterly trusting, like he knew I was coming and now he was safe. Introductions over with, he confidently strutted back towards his mother. I turned to leave and he peeped back at me. I held his eye and he whinnied. He sounded like a baby elephant. I smiled, sending him silent words of comfort and reassurance that we would definitely meet again. He seemed confident we would.

Unfortunately I could only afford to help him and his mother. The other mare was thin but stronger than Wynnie's mum, and the hippies seemed reluctant to let her go as they clearly preferred her. I arranged to bring the mare and Wynnie back to my place. I had left the trail riding centre accommodation and was renting a little farmhouse which sheep had moved out of before I moved in. It had no electricity, toilet, or running water, but it had a well and was surrounded by fruit trees. Most importantly, being close to the canal irrigation system meant it had lots of lovely fertile grass. I hadn't left the trail centre completely, but was now working there on a two weeks on and one week off rota.

I paid the hippies for the foal, nothing more than meat value, and arranged to take the mare free of charge to get her back to health. The vet told me I should have kept her and reported them for neglect, but to whom? Portugal didn't have any kind of animal welfare legislation in those days. Debbie and I once met a man pretending to represent a well-known British horse charity, but when we contacted them they hadn't heard of him. He was actively rescuing horses but couldn't look after them himself.

Now I had Wynnie and his mum to look after. He had to be weaned straight away as his mum didn't have much milk and she needed all her strength. He was around four months old when weaned. He was given a milk pellet substitute from the vet but was eager to eat hard food and grass. His appetite is still the same today, the greediest horse I've ever met. He was such a character and would strike open the door to my little farmhouse with his front hooves and strut around the kitchen to steal food, even venturing into the bedroom to pull the throws off my bed. He was mischievous and would follow me anywhere.

The German hippies came to visit one day and were so impressed with the condition of the mare that they wanted her back straight away. I was powerless to stop them. They didn't pay me for any of the feed or vet treatment I had spent on her and seemed to think I had done it out of charity. I'm just thankful I had Wynnie. I could never have coped if they'd taken him too but thankfully they didn't seem interested, they were almost nervous of him. His character was no push over, unlike his poor mother.

They had arranged transport with Debbie who had her horse lorry in Portugal. She couldn't get the truck anywhere near my house as it was so remote with only rough tracks. I was on a trail when they arrived to take her. Debbie told me it was horrible, the German woman riding the mare across the tracks in a big, heavy shepherd's saddle. But she assured me that their farm did have some grass there after the recent rains, and the other mare and foal were still alive and looking better than when we'd last seen them.

There wasn't really anything I could do, they wanted the horse and that was that. I later heard they had sold the horses on to some Gypsies and the woman had taken the baby and returned home to Germany leaving the man. Their aspirations of living off grid and regressing back to nature were over, like so many other lost souls that tried to do the same. Some succeeded and lived happily but these were usually the ones who had money to begin with. Then there were the ones that became truly lost in the twilight world of drugs, only to die lonely and afraid, their dreams scattered and beaten, then left to rot in the dust. I was lucky, I had a job and the next week I was back on the trails with a full season ahead of me. I had a lovely Portuguese neighbour who would take care of Wynnie and another rescued mare I had also acquired.

Ode to an Olive Tree Shower

It was Thursday and that meant day five of the blue coast trail. Not my favourite day. Hung-over from too much brandy in Odeceixe the night before, and a long ride inland through the blistering heat to look forward to, this was not the easiest of days to cope with. Although very beautiful, Thursday's lunch and night spots had become known as 'The Lunch Spot from Hell' and 'The Nightmare Night Spot'. I was on my own leading the trails now Debbie had left, and feeling the pressure. Not so much the hard work, which I could always manage, but sometimes I found it hard to stay positive and happy for the benefit of the tourists. Some days I needed peace and quiet, with time to reflect. Spending about eight hours a day in the saddle leading a group of tourists and forcing a smile like a children's TV presenter is hard when you're not really feeling it. Some days I just felt down, and then I would wonder what the hell I was doing here.

I'd managed to get through the morning's ride with no mishaps and had suggested the guests all be quiet, as we may get the chance to spot some wild boar. Cork trees twisted their branches lazily across our path, embracing like flamenco dancers, limbs entwined and two toned in colour where the cork had been harvested on some and not others. Their midnight dance was now frozen in the reality of day. The acorns they produced were longer and larger than traditional acorns and adored by the wild boar. In direct contrast to the previous day's dry, stony tracks and the fire breaks of the eucalyptus forests with their sizzling menthol odour from the sticky sap melting in the blistering sunlight, the cork forests were damp and earthy with a wild, woody smell that cooled the senses. We passed a natural spring that had been turned into a boggy pit by the boar that loved to wallow in the rich, brown mud. In between the trees grew tall bushes of white flowering heather that rustled as sleepy boars rested and grunted in their shade.

With the serene coolness of the tranquil cork forest behind us, we arrived at The Lunch Spot From Hell which was at the side of a track and the nearest place the jeep and trailer could get to.

Lunch was prepared in the usual way with wooden boards laid out on top of wooden trestles to form a large table. The white plastic chairs were arranged invitingly around the cool box which was full of cold drinks and beer for the guests. Some kind of meat dish would have been expertly prepared by the cook, a lovely Portuguese woman with thick, curly, black hair. She always made me laugh and in turn would laugh hysterically back until her false teeth fell out. "I wonder what happened to Fernanda's front teeth," I asked Debbie one day.

"She used to be a prostitute," Debbie replied. "It was her pimp and boyfriend that punched her in the face and knocked them out."

"Bloody hell!" I said quite shocked. "That's awful."

"Apparently she was lucky to get away from him alive," said Debbie.

I'd never questioned her myself, about her life, but I could tell that behind her laughing eyes lay painful memories. When I feel like times are hard, even now, I think back to what she must have gone through and how she was a survivor.

Being vegetarian I got to eat heated up beans. Not baked beans of the Heinz variety or even a close reproduction. I'm talking a tin of either white or red kidney beans warmed in a pan – sometimes with an onion chopped up and mixed in as an added bonus. I was always so hungry by this time, that I hardly tasted it anyway. The horses would be tethered to stackers, as there were no substantial trees at The Lunch Spot From Hell. Instead the ground was covered with spiky plants. Spiky, spiny thistles grew everywhere, making it impossible to relax, not that I had any chance of being able to do so. Walking through them, even with the thick leather Portuguese riding chaps which I always wore, didn't help, as somehow the spiky bits would work their way under the leather to poke painfully through my cotton jodhpurs.

Richard and Nancy would have stressfully (Richard) and tearfully (Nancy) prepared all of this before our arrival. She only stayed because she cared about him, but he never noticed. He would then open a beer as if he hadn't a care in the world and turn his smiling face towards the tired guests and begin to work his Irish charm. He was an excellent actor.

"Hi, you wonderful people, welcome to your lunch!" he would cry out enthusiastically and prance about like some dandy fop. I would rush around taking tired horses from exhausted guests, after having quickly secured my own. I'd then have to think fast to attach horses next to horses that tolerated each other, in order to avoid a kicking match. As the guests collapsed into chairs I'd remove the horses' tack and carefully place the saddles onto the wooden trestles, and then hang the sweaty saddle blankets up, as God forbid they fall onto the spiky hell underfoot.

The horses would be fed and watered and before having a chance to fully recover it would be time to begin brushing the dried sweat off, a second round of water and then to saddle up again. The guests didn't usually partake in helping, as they were still exhausted. Although some would try, it was quicker to do it myself; as at least I knew it had been done correctly then. Once all the horses were ready, we would head off inland once more towards The Nightmare Nightspot, which was located on the banks of the river Mira, just outside the picturesque town of Odemira.

For some reason this particular trail was taking its toll on me. I had about ten guests so having coped alone night and day with eleven horses I suppose it was normal to feel exhausted. I was also riding a new mare called Estrella, who was really unstable and basically insane. I always got to ride the horses that were deemed unsuitable for the guests. She was a very pretty little bay mare but being a lead horse was not the most confidence-giving start to her trail riding career. One minute I would be going forwards calmly and collectedly and the next I would be careering sideways through all sorts of undergrowth uphill or downhill with no regards to looming cliff edges. I would frantically yell over my shoulder to the terrified guest next in line, "Stay on the track! Do not follow me!"

Branches would whip past my face as I struggled to get her under control. The Germans would mutter together and the

Americans would whoop and yell 'Ye Ha!' thinking it was all part of the entertainment. Sometimes I'd feel her stumble and I'd think we'd both had it, but somehow we survived. Then she would almost click back into her calm self and wonder what the hell she was doing halfway up a mountain or halfway down a cliff. Neighing frantically, she'd scramble back towards the other horses to take our place at the front again.

"Terribly sorry," I'd say. "I don't know what happened, but if it happens again just continue along the track." Months later she gave birth to a mule; we had no idea she was pregnant and obviously hormonal during this time.

I was dreading the ride into Odemira town, where we would cross the main road river bridge. As the guide and trail leader I would be first in line defiantly holding my hand up in a 'stop now' signal to oncoming trucks that filled the bridge. I used to feel like Gandalf the wizard facing the Balrog on the bridge of Khazad Dum in Moria. Unfortunately, I didn't have the same confidence in my schizophrenic little mare as I would with one of the other horses. Thankfully by the time we reached the bridge she was exhausted and there were no big trucks – or Balrogs – to challenge us.

Turning off the main road onto a track along the riverside we would dismount and lead our tired horses towards The Nightmare Nightspot. Just like magic, the night spot would have been stressfully and tearfully prepared in advance by a triumphant Richard and an exhausted Nancy. It was based at a cluster of old disused farm buildings. This meant some horses were able to spend the night indoors tethered to rings in old stone mangers alongside each other. To prevent them beating each other up, poles would be hung carefully from the rafters as barriers.

Although a welcome break from the sun, the barns here were cramped and dark, with low ceilings. Clean straw for bedding would be spread out on top of the dried dung floor. Every horse, encouraged by the rustling noise, would pee into the deep straw, letting out deep groans of relief, the smell of ammonia stifling. I think I properly stunk of it but just got used to it. The rest of the horses would be tethered on long lines attached from the corner of one of the buildings and then to a tree. Others were simply tethered to anything deemed remotely suitable to tether them to. A proper nightmare.

The small fact of where I would sleep sometimes escaped my boss's attention, this particular night being one of them. After unsaddling and watering the horses I decided to pitch my small two-man tent inside the barn in a corner area that had probably been used for a small mule or donkey. The floor was soft with years of dried droppings that gave off a sweet and not particularly unpleasant aroma. I only put up the internal fly sheet of the tent, and unrolled my bed roll ready. I'd learnt how to separate myself from my surroundings, as if I was merely looking at them from behind the safety of a thick unbreakable glass screen. I honestly believe that if I has looked closely at the insects and huge spiders crawling across the stone walls and floor, their legs jerking awkwardly as they navigated strands of straw and dried droppings – and then at night, the unseen but not unheard rats and mice that scurried around squeaking as they squabbled – I would most probably have gone insane.

After having only managed a bucket wash the previous night, the one thing the lovely town of Odemira had to offer was public showers. This kept my spirits up; the thought of being able to have a proper shower for a handful of escudos to wash the dirt and sweat away, was pure bliss. With the horses all seen to, I set off with my small rucksack containing toiletries and a change of clothing on my back. As I passed some fields I saw the locals busy harrowing the dry dusty land with a mule pulling a wooden harrow. The air was full of choking dust particles that stuck cloyingly to the sweat on my skin. They waved at me and we exchanged pleasantries. I explained in my not so great Portuguese that I was going into the town for a much-needed shower. They replied with cries of *Ferias* and *Festa!* I thought they were talking about a party they would have after work, so I laughed and smiled whilst continuing on my way, and they stared – rather bewildered – after me.

The town of Odemira was built into the hillside that led up from the river with the public showers located near the very top. Powered on by the thought of clean, warm water cascading over me I trudged up the hill. The perspiration was running down my back, my leather Australian hat was stuck to my head I'd sweated that much under it. I could feel my skin burning in the late afternoon sun. As I passed the street cafes, I could smell the strong coffee, and even though I was vegetarian, my mouth still watered shamelessly at the salty sour smell of smoked ham suspended from wooden platters on the bars. It looked repulsive to me, with the trotter left on and the skin a dark jaundiced yellow half carved away to reveal the dark red dry meat inside, but it was enjoyed by the locals. There was a lot of music playing and the bars seemed to be busier than usual, with smiling people raising their glasses as I trudged past.

I sighed with relief to see the old dark green painted wooden doors to the public showers. I almost skipped up the steps and then crashed smack into them. They were locked. I pushed at them in disbelief, some of the paint crumbling off and sticking to my sweaty palms. Then it dawned on me. The reason there had been no trucks to threaten our bridge crossing and the reason the locals had been shouting *festa* and *ferias* to me when I'd told them I was heading to the showers, was because it was a holiday. That meant they were closed.

Exhausted and deflated I turned and trudged back down the hill and into the nearest café. I ordered a *tosta de quejo* (toasted cheese sandwich buttered on both sides of the bread), with a *golao* (espresso coffee and foamed milk), with a full glass of brandy croft on the side. Cursing the Portuguese habit of closing things on holidays I chose a shady, smoke filled corner inside the café to sit down; I'd had enough fresh air and sunlight. Some of the old men at the bar nodded at me before returning to their treacle like espressos and *cigante* cigarettes. I suppose I looked like a farm worker, just like them, except I was probably dirtier. After a refreshing glass of my customary life-saving liquid of *agua das pedras* (sparkling water) to wash the brandy down I set off back to the horses.

The locals were still harrowing their field but were having a break when I passed and offered me a beer. I declined and they told me again that the showers were closed. (The Portuguese have a great habit of stating the obvious.) They gestured at me to follow them; rather confused I wondered what they were on about when a large Portuguese mamma came bustling around the side of the house and called me round. I obliged and realised she was offering for me to shower at her house. I was so relieved and enamoured by the friendliness of the Portuguese – then I realised they were a very poor family and the shower was basically a hose pipe hanging out of the olive tree by the back door, with a shower head stuffed into the end of it.

The Portuguese mamma told me to get undressed and shower there, and she'd make sure the lads in the field didn't peep. I didn't know what to do; I desperately wanted to get clean so throwing caution to the wind I stripped off and showered as fast as I could. I remember balancing my little bottle of shampoo in the olive tree as I struggled to rinse the bubbles out of my matted hair. The shower hose kept falling out of the tree, and in the end she held it over me to rinse the shampoo and soap away. Every so often she would yell obscenities at the farm workers who were trying to look, and I could hear them giggling. I was mortified. What the hell was I doing? My previous life and existence seemed very far away.

It was most definitely a moment in time I will never forget. Feeling refreshed and clean I thanked her and accepted a beer which I drank back at my camp. I explained I needed to return to the horses. I'll not forget sitting outside the old barn where my tent was pitched brushing the knots out of my hair whilst the horses snoozed contentedly. Without any mobile phones or social media it was certainly a very lonely place for me. I longed to speak to my friends and family and tell them, "You'll never guess what, some big Portuguese mamma just hosed me down under her olive tree!" I wondered what my Mum would say, and my sister. What would they think if they saw me now? Would they even care what I'd experienced? Tracie, my best friend I'd grown up with, was married with her second child on the way.

It dawned on me that I was longing for normality. I was in a wonderland hoping to find myself, but where was I really? Who was I? Would my family and friends even know me now? I'd been away for two years riding through wild and wonderful countryside, sleeping in a tent or in a barn at night. My closest companions were horses, my attempt at a serious relationship had been – unbeknown to me – with a heroin addict which had thankfully failed miserably, but I'd survived. My other relationships had been nothing but meaningless fun with boys too good looking for their own good, not any I'd wanted to get seriously involved with.

Now I felt different, like I was ready for the real world again. Life here was not really working for me anymore. I wasn't happy just flitting around in some strange surreal Otherworld. If I wasn't careful I would be in danger of drifting through another few years, and for what? I wanted to step out of this bittersweet fairy land and get back on the merry go round of life, back to the real world. It was time for me to go home. With that thought in mind I did a final check on the horses and, trying not to let my head torch shine on the crawling nightlife surrounding my little tent, I collapsed onto my bedroll. The old mule, long dead, whose dried droppings my tent rested upon, gazed wistfully at me as I drifted off to sleep.

Follow the Comet Home

Needless to say, my announcement that I was planning on leaving didn't go down well with Richard and I stayed well into the winter, my last trail being the Christmas Star trail. It was a melancholy time that created a deep and meaningful memory that will stay forever. It was Christmas Eve and we were camped on the Atlantic coast, tucked into the edge of a woody glen sheltered behind the dunes. The night was cloudy and a mist hung low over the trees. I couldn't see the stars but the dreamy miasma had its own otherworldliness eclipsing all outside sound, leaving just the contented munching of the horses, as they tucked into their piles of hay after the long ride, and the rise and fall of the winter sea.

I sat at the entrance of my tiny tent smoking a joint whilst thinking back to the previous spring. The comet Hale Bopp was clearly visible in the sky and I had sat in this very place then, smoking a joint, admiring it. Was there a spaceship hidden in its tail? Was it gathering the souls of those stupid, or brave enough, to have killed themselves at its passing – hoping to be picked up and taken to a higher plane? What I saw was a magical sight of sheer wonder. Even now I think back to it, eager to relive such a glorious moment. I couldn't have chosen a better spot to witness it. Mediterranean pine trees silhouetted against a backdrop of a Portuguese sky, the sound of the Atlantic Ocean, horse sweat and sweet manure blending enticingly with the salty smell of the sea and the sharp fresh scent of coastal herbs that crunched underfoot.

Tonight it held a different beauty. Hale Bopp may still have been dimly visible but I was not looking to the stars. I was enjoying the warm comfort of being enveloped within my little circle of munching, farting horses. It was a cosy atmosphere and I walked around stopping to pat and stroke each one in turn. They had told me their own tales of woe. Each of them had come from a bad life where they had suffered at the hands of man. These trails were hard work but there was a comradeship where we all worked together. I looked after them and they looked after me. I didn't want to tell them I was leaving. I would miss each and every quirky one of them. I went to the food store and began to gather more forage. They all looked over expectantly; some whinnied quietly, others nickered and some just pawed the ground impatiently, creating clouds of sandy dust.

"Calm down," I told them. "I've only got one pair of hands," and laughing I gave them all extra. Well it was Christmas. I got into my sleeping bag but left my tent flap tied open; sitting up I opened my little flask of brandy, bought especially for the occasion, and whilst sipping the fiery substance I thought about my childhood and relaxed, my eyes half closing as I began to doze. Here there was no tree decked with baubles and coloured lights but plenty of fir trees garlanded by the misty haze and between the trees Christmas Eve arrived, her skirts twirling and billowing as she danced across the land. The real horses on their long line tethers slowly finished eating and they too relaxed into sleep, their souls cavorting like paper horse garlands that frolicked into my dreams as I floated along to the continuous rise and fall of the winter sea.

Soon after this trail I was ready to leave. I was paying Debbie to drive me and Wynnie home along with the other rescued mare I had managed to re-home in the UK. I said goodbye to my few friends, some laughing and calling me a Gypsy because wherever I went my horses went too. Debbie had professionally prepared the small English horse lorry to accommodate us and her motorbike too, which she was taking home. Various overnight stops along the way were arranged, which thankfully went according to plan. I was looking forward to emerging from the rabbit hole and joining normality again – hopefully I would not get shot down by it.

Hell

As my brain caught up with reality and the terrifying realisation of where I was, I surveyed my surroundings. The cell was disgusting. It had an old foam mattress, with a rough mustard-coloured woollen blanket and an old fashioned yellow striped and stained feather pillow. It smelled musty and sour. A policeman opened a sealed plastic bag and gave me a thin, almost papery, sheet to put over myself to sleep. I kept begging them to tell me what I had done. It was terrifying not knowing what I was being punished for.

Through the night I lay in a state of shock, wrapped in the paper sheet drifting in and out of deranged nightmares clutching the scrap of paper with the drawing of Caramello and me Tessa had done on the plane. Needing the toilet I struggled to open my eyes and realised I'd been crying so much they had swollen and I could hardly see. I stood up and called out. My voice was so weak I didn't know if anyone could hear me. I tried to knock on the bars but this made little noise. I took a deep breath and wailed "Please somebody hear me." The kind policeman who had given me the tablet arrived. He couldn't look me in the eye and when he did I saw a flash of pity before he averted his glaze.

"Toilet?" I said, my voice tiny and fearful.

"Oui," he replied and indicated for me to follow once he had unlocked the steel barred door. He escorted me down the corridor to a small bathroom. All the while he held his automatic weapon at the ready. They seemed to be on high alert here, after the recent terrorist attacks I supposed. I closed the bathroom door, there was no lock and he stood guard outside. I looked into the small plastic mirror above the wash basin and saw my eyes hiding behind two mouths. My eyelids had swollen so badly they looked like pouting silicone lips wobbling back at me, my terrified pupils concealed within.

I was returned to my cell and lay down, willing myself to be anywhere except in that cell. I should have been sitting on Susan's balcony enjoying a glass of wine watching Tessa enjoy her first holiday abroad. They called a doctor for me during the early hours; I believe I was suffering a panic attack. I remember asking for ice for my head and face, I was so hot and unused to the heat. "No ice," he said. "I give you a tranquilliser to calm you and if you stop crying the swelling in your eyes will go down... but then everybody cries in jail, eh! Eh heh heh." His mocking laughter lingered long after he'd left.

I closed my eyes. After Portugal I'd been happy to be back in Wales, but soon I'd gone in search of my dreams again, chasing the Holy Grail – but at least I'd found Caramello, my beautiful Spanish stallion. I looked at Tessa's little drawing and remembered a story I once told to Hannah, a young girl who originally came to me for work experience with horses, and subsequently became a good friend.

Spirit horse

Once upon a time, when I am tired and old, I wonder what will be left of me when I die, except maybe a cadaver exposed on the mortuary slab. No soul on show, just glistening viscera. There is a clattering outside. My heart palpitates and I pull myself out of bed – but something's not right – my legs feel leaden. It's a frightening sensation. I drag my body down the stairs. Am I turning to stone? I wonder – my punishment for stealing from the stone dwarves when I was a child. I make it to the living room; the photographs hanging on the wall suddenly stand out, clear. They are mostly of horses and a cluster of my daughter smiling and laughing. I am there smiling with her, and in others performing on my horses, moments of glory captured forever, surrounded in gilt or wood.

The fireplace is cold, the log burner clean and unlit. I've been using an electric heater at night for extra warmth; it's easier than struggling with lighting a fire at my age. My eyes move to the wall above the fireplace, where immortalised in oil and adorned in a medieval gown of blue and gold trimmed with faux ermine, I sit serene and composed astride a white horse that is equally unperturbed. He elegantly raises one forefoot to match the opposite hind leg in the classical outline of a collected piaffe. I've not looked at this painting for such a long time but something has drawn my attention… its beauty is remarkable. The sound comes again, startling me like hoof beats on tarmac, odd as I don't keep horses anymore. Maybe it's just someone riding past. Intrigued, I peer through the glass of the front door and see my old Spanish stallion. He's jumped out of the oil painting to land, hooves clattering in the yard.

I pause in my storytelling for effect. It works. Hannah has stopped preparing dinner and is looking at me eagerly, awaiting my next instalment. "Go on, what happens next, don't stop now, was it Caramello?" I smile and refill my glass with a fresh crisp Chardonnay from a bag in a box. Savouring the first mouthful I prop my feet up on the table and continue my tale.

Shocked at the sight of this white horse I grapple for the door handle, my stone arms struggling. It opens soundlessly, I hardly touch it… and then I am no longer turning to stone. Like a sprite I rush towards him, my hands caressing his silken neck, my fingers tangle in his mane where it cascades over his shoulder. His coat is soft, his muscles hard and strong, and he is not ravaged by the cancer that took him. I feel myself laughing and I'm crying too as I vault effortlessly onto his back.

My thighs are smooth and tanned, my muscles strong again as they grip his sides. I realise I am barefoot and I wriggle my toes into his warm fur as the icy numbness I've suffered for years melts. Before we disappear into the greenwood of legend where I can hear other familiar neighs on the breeze, a small tug, as if I've snagged myself in a bramble and pulled free, jerks me and I look back. There, slumped in the doorway of my little cottage, is the body of a frail, gray haired old woman. Around her neck a silver chain... the pendant of braided horsehair my daughter gave me for Christmas.

I get up to help Hannah with the dinner. "That's so sad," she says, wiping tears from her eyes. "Is that what you think will truly happen?" Laughing I finish my wine.

"It's only a story Hannah, a fairy tale."

Quest for the Holy Grail: To the North!

Being home was not all I had imagined. Wynnie was a yearling and terribly naughty. I kept him at my parent's house but soon had to move him. He had watched the oil tank delivery man deliver about two hundred pounds worth of central heating oil. When the chap had gone he leant over the wall and with his nose – that at times resembled a tapir's snout, so inclined was it to get into mischief – he unscrewed the cap, letting half the oil flood across the floor. My father was livid. He had been watching him from the dining room window but didn't get out in time once he'd realised what the bugger was up to. Wynnie, however, just galloped and sprang around the field in delight. He would watch my mother hanging out the washing and then stretch over the wall, his nose taking on the tapir form, and pull the clean sheets into the field. He'd thoroughly enjoy tearing about dragging the clean washing through the mud with my mum having to bribe him with food to get it back. He was such a little tyrant.

I hadn't found any proper work yet. I was desperate to learn more and to put my new-found knowledge of classical riding into practice. I was also realising I had a much greater gift than this. I had a connection with horses. I could attune to their thoughts and feelings. I had picked this up by living and working in such close proximity with these mighty beasts. Horses empower you to look inside yourself; you can't lie to them. If you are fearful then outward acts of confidence will not work because they know what you feel on the inside. In their innocent way horses demand honesty and in turn they do not judge. It's okay to reveal your innermost self to the horse because they can already see it. This knowledge was what helped me to help my greatest teacher, Caramello – the Spanish devil.

Wynnie was too young to do much more with. He could be led, brushed and rugged, allow his feet to be trimmed, loaded into a trailer and lorry, and came to me whenever I called, demanding huge Wynnie bear hugs. In fact, what he hadn't experienced much of was living like a horse with other horses. So in order for me to move away for work I took him to a livery yard down on my beloved Gower coast. There he would be on grass livery, living with other horses. It was spring and by the following winter I would arrange for him to come to me so I could start his training and prepare him for backing.

I was living with a friend, Martin, who I cared about and respected. Unfortunately, I wasn't ready to settle down although the two years I spent with him on returning from Portugal, on reflection, were some of the happiest of my life. But I had to keep moving. I was on a quest and not entirely sure what I was questing for. I replied to an advertisement I saw in *Horse and Hound* magazine. It was for jousting knights. How random, I thought. Much to my delight they were also looking for a Lady Gwenhyfawr to ride their Spanish horses.

I received a phone call and couldn't believe my luck: I was invited for an interview. Martin was supportive but reluctant to move with me, as it was a live-in position. He was happy being close to his friends and family and I could not expect him to leave them. If I did get the job, which I was confident I would, I'd be on my own again. He promised to visit me, which he did, but it was quite some distance from South Wales to the North of England. The M6 has never been an easy motorway to drive and I believe we both knew it would never work.

Undeterred by distance and leaving my friends again, I set off for my interview. It was an odd affair. My future new boss was clearly more interested in what I looked like; I don't suppose he wanted an unsightly Gwenhyfawr. I must have passed this test as I was then taken to see the horses. I rode a lovely bay stallion that was trained very well in the art of *haute école*, a highly trained form of dressage. Then I rode a beautiful mare that appeared terribly stressed but still performed the movements if not a little too tensely for my liking. Then the two chaps, my new boss included, looked nervous and gave me a head collar and asked me to get the big white stallion out.

The end stall contained a magnificent beast of glistening silver, apart from the stable stains and the fact he looked like he hadn't had a proper grooming for some time. I opened the door and was surprised to see the two men take a step backwards. The horse immediately flattened his ears. I ignored this and approached him innocently, placing the head collar on, and looked at the others to see why they were looking so frightened.

"Just lead him out and walk him around and then put him back," said my new boss. The other chap whispered a warning, "Watch him, have your wits about you, he can be nasty." I led the beautiful stallion out. Straight away I felt him prance and he screamed out a neigh, pulling at the rope in order to get to the other horses. I kept a tight hold of him and spoke gently but firmly. He was so eager and surprised to be out of his stable that I think he was too shocked to properly misbehave. Then I turned him and led him back in.

"Shall I put his tack on?" I asked.

"No, leave him for now," said my new boss. "There's plenty of time for you to get acquainted with him." So that was that. We discussed the formalities and I was shown my accommodation, a lovely large static caravan. I was to start the following month. I was off on my travels once again. Saying goodbye to my friends was sad but I was heading for Camelot on a quest for the Holy Grail. I failed to notice how happy my present situation had been in my eagerness to set off on my travels once again. Even so, my mood was positive and I was excited; another adventure was coming my way.

Welcome to the Kingdom

I worked with a great bunch of people. They were typically Northern and had a sense of humour I wasn't quite used to but I managed to hold my own. The entertainers, which we were, all lived in the static caravan accommodation at the edge of the theme park. The noise of the rides being tested when the park was closed was particularly eerie, empty carts whizzing around, no screams or music just the groaning and grinding of the engines and screeching of the wind. Even walking through the park to get down to the stables, which were in a no public access area, meant walking through them. I've always been frightened of fairground rides, even the small ones for young children. To me they look sinister. When the park was open it was noisy and full of life. Screams and laughter would fill the air sounding nothing like the empty ghost town it became during winter.

I settled in before the park opened and made friends. The Knights of the Round Table were not as chivalrous as legend has it and usually left the majority of the mucking out to me. Lancelot, obviously, was lovely, as was Gawain and they became good friends. The black knight Mordred and his wife were friendly and welcoming too. King Arthur was a gentleman until my boss took over the role which made him a bit of a rogue.

At first I was the only female but was told Fluffy would be returning soon. She'd been there longer than me, a beautiful ballerina who played the part of Morgan le Fey, Merlin the Magician's assistant. She had a caravan next to mine and we became firm friends. After work we would open a couple of cans of ale whilst listening to music sharing cigarettes and Camelot gossip. I think I introduced her to Black Sabbath.

The jousting arena, where I would perform on the horses, was a brightly painted colourful affair of red, green and gold. On one long side it had seating for about two thousand people. The other side was a theatrical medieval backdrop that held a raised platform and King Arthur's throne. I would work with the jesters to perform during the halfway point of the joust. It was something I'd never done before. Riding and schooling a horse classically is one thing but this was more like circus performance. The horses knew their job and were fantastic. The Spanish mare, I realised, did not enjoy herself the same as the elderly bay stallion who was now too old to perform in the two shows a day every day which was the demand through the summer season.

The jesters were great and helped me to adjust and fit in to what was needed of me and the horses. It pretty much meant performing a variety of *haute école* or circus movements to music whilst dressed up in costume as Lady Gwenhyfawr. As the jesters were dancing and acting ridiculous alongside me it was more a humorous than a serene or elegant performance, but it was meant to be funny. Keeping the horses' attention and asking them to go through the movements day after day was nerve-racking. Quickly I realised the pretty Spanish mare was not going to last the season. She was getting fed up and I did not want to have to force her into anything. She had performed numerous previous seasons before I had arrived. Making her perform went against the grain of everything I believed in, and I was feeling more and more uncomfortable. The glorious white stallion would have to take over.

Royal Horse or Demon Spawn

I had now been properly told about Caramello. He was a disturbed beast and had previously only been handled by one of the lads who had worked there and then left. The stallion was violent. He had probably been trained and treated very badly in Spain, from where he originated. He appeared to hate people and himself. I would catch him attacking his own shoulder, biting it until it bled. He would throw himself repeatedly against his stable wall bashing his shoulders and gnashing his teeth. The front of his stable had bars across it and over the stable door so he could not put his head out. If he did, anyone standing on the other side might lose their face. He had apparently bitten the previous girl very badly.

This angry beast was going to have to be Lady Gwenhyfawr's new mount, and apart from that one fault he was perfect for the job – absolutely drop dead gorgeous. Horses are never called white, they are always referred to as grey because they are born a colour from which the grey gene greys out, until eventually they become white, but rarely pure white. Caramello was a pure pearlescent white, like angel wings – or a fallen angel, more like. His temperament was so terrible he hadn't been used in the shows for a long time. He had proved difficult to sell too, for the same reason. So his life was reduced to being led out to the jousting arena in the early mornings, before anyone arrived, to have a leg stretch and sniff about and then shut behind bars for the rest of the day and night. No wonder he behaved so badly.

This was a horrific existence for such a magnificent being. I'm sure they would have found a solution for him soon, as it was not practical for him to be there, but it fell to me to give him one last attempt at doing the shows. I set about trying to rehabilitate him and change his life. First, I would have to be able to handle him without being attacked. Some days he would behave too dangerously to try and get a head collar on him, let alone lead him past the other horses. This would have to change. I was going to handle him regularly every day, grooming him and bathing him, which he learned to love.

To begin with I needed to become his friend and not the enemy. I thought about when I first met Wynnie. That had been instant, a connection that had been made between us in an unspoken language. I thought about the wild ponies I had encountered at the rescue centre where I used to work. They were different again; they were wild and saw us humans as predators. Gaining their trust was like undoing evolution. They had evolved to think this way and it took time to convince them we were not hunting them but taking care of them. Horses are far from stupid and those that wanted to learn and adapt did; these would usually be the youngsters. Older horses were happy to simply accept us, but kept their guard up. Caramello was not a wild untamed horse or a youngster anymore. He was in his teens and had encountered something terrible in his life to make him hate people so much.

To begin with I would enter his stable, ignore him and sit on the floor eating polo mints. He would fly at me in a rage and stop just short of touching me. I realised he didn't really want to hurt me but to taunt me into reacting, which I didn't. When he calmed, almost forgetting I was there, I would quickly and silently leave the stable closing the door behind me. His first instinct would be wonder at where I was going so quickly and why? Then rage at having missed his opportunity to bite me on the way out. I did this a few times but one day his face was close to mine (much like the scene from the *Alien* movie with me being Sigourney Weaver). I opened my palm and offered him a polo mint. This threw him. He was enraged, yet also inquisitive enough to want to know what I had been eating. He sniffed my hand, intrigued. I thought he would eat it but he stopped. Instead he hurled his body at the wall crashing against it like he was trying to knock it down. I left and closed the door.

The next time we made some progress. He took the polo mint, crunching it gently, nodding his head and familiarising himself with the taste and texture. It was at this moment I felt him exhale deeply. I placed my palm upon his brow and slowly stroked him, moving his forelock out of his eyes. He stayed there for quite a few minutes. Soon I would need to start riding him, so when I was confident I carried his tack over to the stable. I groomed him and tacked him up with no trouble and led him out. He began to prance and scream at the other horses. I imagined him saying, "My name is Caramello, King of Kings; Look on my works, ye Mighty and despair!"

But unlike *Ozymandias* in Shelly's famous poem, Caramello was not a crumbling statue. He was a living breathing King. I mounted up, with trepidation, but he stood calmly as I lowered myself into the saddle and we walked forward. Now I fully understood why these Iberian horses were the royal horses of Europe. There was no other way to sit except with pride. I had ridden this breed before but never had I sat on anything as magnificent as Caramello.

I breathed in deeply and matched my breath to his strides as we warmed up, turning and flexing. At first he was a little stiff; this was understandable, but he would soon loosen up with regular classical schooling exercises. We then trotted and cantered, his paces so smooth we seemed to glide across the arena. There was no rushing or pulling, he was steady with a beautiful natural balance to his paces. The lighter I was with my hands and legs the more he responded. Then, as if by magic, he floated into the mesmerising gait that is called the *passage.* This is a *collected*, or elevated, trot involving a moment of suspension, appearing as a majestic dance between horse and rider. When forced it is an unpleasant sight but when performed naturally it is a dream to behold.

I held my breath as we floated across the arena, the colours of the jousting tilt rail a blur. I was afraid to breathe in case I interrupted this mystical dance. I felt overwhelmed and, not wanting to do too much in one go, I brought him back to a walk. Leaning over his neck I patted him over and over telling him what an incredible and magnificent horse he was. He walked freely in a few circles on a loose rein and we went for a hack around the theme park. I couldn't stop smiling and I believe he had enjoyed himself too. His ears were forward and his eyes bright and alert. I would come to ride him out often through our life together and I have never felt safer or happier than on his back. One of my favourite views is between those pearly white ears.

He wasn't always such an obliging horse though. Once I lowered my guard and opened the bars above his stable door. He had been so calm and almost loving whilst I had been grooming him. He had been left tied but knew how to undo the quick release knots used for safety. When I returned, carrying his tack to place it on the floor beside his door, his head came over the top, ears flattened, lips peeled back and with teeth bared, punched me between the shoulders. The force knocked me to the floor winding me terribly. I was shaken and frightened; a horse had never physically and deliberately hurt me before, nor with such malice. I quickly replaced the bars and carried his tack away, leaving him biting his shoulder and throwing himself into the wall. For today the demon was in residence.

It was difficult to understand how he had such a split personality. I decided much of it was caused from boredom and from being shut up in a stable for so long. So I arranged for him to have some proper turnout. My boss said he could go out into the old deer park, which was a large safe area with a high secure fence. There were no deer there anymore. At first he refused to leave the gate, almost panicking. I decided to leave him to it, give him some space. When I came back he had hidden himself between part of a hawthorn hedge and the outer fence, getting stuck. I had to get help to remove him, he'd cut himself on the hawthorn, an angry splash of red against white. He was clearly experiencing a horse form of agoraphobia and was more messed up than I had originally realised. I led him back to his stable and he came willingly, almost meekly.

"Maybe not the big field for you again, hey boy?" I said to him. He was a wise, battle-scarred warrior suffering the traumatic effects that life had dished out to him. I understood him more now. His eyes blinked at me in acknowledgment, for there was no demon in his eyes today and that evil would stay away for longer periods of time, although it never truly left him. His eyes were like windows and sometimes my wise warrior looked out at me, but at other times something dark was waiting and would peer at me from behind his eyes. The horse I knew and loved would not be present; he would be cowering in fear, hiding from the same demon staring at me with hatred. That's when even I would do something else before coming back to him, hoping it had gone.

Soon Caramello was performing well in the shows. I was making progress and he adored showing off to a crowd of people and it was wonderful to see. He was exquisitely trained and taught me much about the classical dressage movements, of which I was merely a novice in comparison, but eager to learn. He still had his bad moments, which I believe was more to do with his surroundings. This would involve him attacking the tilt rail during our shows. One minute he would be performing with ease and the next he'd be trying to get hold of one of the jesters that were behind the rail. I think the audience found it amusing but it became more and more frequent. He was fed up with Camelot. I understood this, as the magical kingdom was beginning to get to me too – in a bad way.

I was exhausted and stressed out. The same show twice a day every day was tedious and left me dazed. The season when in full flow, left you with no time to think about anything else and two seasons were enough for me. I also didn't fancy spending another long cold winter there working as maintenance and taking care of the horses. Fluffy was leaving and going to work on the cruise ships and there was talk that the park may close. I would need to think carefully about my future and that of my horses, Wynnie, and now Caramello. He would come with me when I left and for this I would be eternally thankful to my boss. Unfortunately, when I should have known better, I made a big mistake.

The Troll

I'm not sure how it happened. How I stopped listening to myself. Camelot had become a merry-go-round, except I wasn't feeling merry. I was dizzy and confused and really I should have yelled, *Stop! I want to get off*, but I didn't. I kept on spinning around and around. The decision to leave was not my wisest choice. Leave Camelot, yes, this was good, as Caramello and Wynnie would come with me. Leaving everything I found familiar to head off for a new start, with a professional hoodwinker, in a foreign country, was not a good move.

I should have listened to my intuition instead of being so blinded by wanting more and striving for something I hadn't found yet, but I didn't know what I was looking for. Round and round I went in my waltz for adventure, taking my trusty steeds with me – and they trusted me. I just wish I could have trusted me. Maybe I was looking for love and to be loved, neither of which I found – although I believed I had, and convinced myself that I was in love and that he loved me. I fell earnestly for him, because I wanted to, needed to, but it simply led to a life of denial until I was stuck. The web pulled tight and there was no getting away.

Joel did not resemble a troll to begin with. It was only when I got stronger and whatever spell had entranced me, and kept me spinning in a state of confusion, finally released me that I saw his true form. I'm not excusing myself and blaming it on some kind of glamour, but I ignored my own feelings. Later that inner voice became a scream and then a wail. I had no choice then but to listen. How could an intelligent woman like me not see it coming? He had rained his way into my life, a deluge of negativity and confusion drenching me until I was saturated, his toxic clouds extinguishing my sunshine until I was lost in his shadow. But I didn't see it happening.

I dreamed a dream, one I had always been too scared to admit. A dream of falling in love, of being with someone and having that someone want me, love me . . . but I was falling for make believe. I had always pushed people away in the past, didn't want anyone getting too close, I'd never been ready for anything serious. At first I pushed Joel away, I didn't want him invading my space, but the more I pushed the more he pushed back, bouldering through my defences until I questioned them and left them scattered at my feet not caring to rebuild but innocently needing to experience this new defenceless self.

"My ex-wife didn't love me." "She spent all my money; I worked every day for her benefit." These were just some of the excuses he gave in his French accent as he sat on the floor of my caravan, his meagre possessions in bin bags. "I have to bankrupt my company to prevent her from taking everything." I remember some semblance of my old self at this point struggling to hold my defences in place, and this sort of grown up crap was new to me. I was nowhere near feeling adult enough to contemplate marriage and children. I was nearly thirty years old, but I was an independent spirit; horses were my life, not men. I'd had boyfriends and sexual relations, but I'd never believed I'd marry any of them. I'd not had a relationship last longer than about two years. My last serious one was with Martin, the most honest guy I'd ever met, but I'd stupidly left him in my quest for the Holy Grail.

"Well you can't stay here," I said. "There just isn't the space." His face crumpled and I thought he would cry. I felt embarrassed for his sake and cross at myself for appearing cold hearted. So I quickly added, "I suppose a few days will be okay until you find somewhere else."

It wasn't just a few days. It was enough time for me to become entangled in his words. The warning signs I'd noticed first about him, the negative vibes I'd sensed I began to make excuses for. I wasn't experienced enough to know what emotional red flags were let alone heed them, and that's when I allowed my dream to break free and my defences to fall.

I was intrigued by him. Even when I was sure his moving into my caravan was temporary there was a part of me that thought differently. I assumed I was in control as it wasn't a dizzying love at first sight kind of thing, but something was happening to me. I wanted to share my life, feel that someone was there for me. I didn't have to do this life thing all alone, maybe he *was* the one, the only man who had made me truly feel this way. I could lean on him. He laughed and smiled; things I stressed about washed over him. He was a reassuring presence, like we didn't have a care in the world now we were together.

I worked hard at Camelot, really pushed myself, and this invasion into my life was exhausting but I couldn't see that he was the cause. I would return to my caravan to a meal he had prepared for me. I was always starving after work and would rather have cooked what I felt like eating. I tried telling him but he would look so crestfallen that I'd have to express how pleased I was that I didn't have to cook and when I thought about it, I was. I needed to hand over the reins for a bit and be thankful for what he'd made me, whether I felt like some elaborate creation he had attempted or not.

He tried really hard to please which resulted in too rich, creamy foods laced with smelly cheeses when I'd just wanted some simple soup out of a tin with bread and normal cheddar. One day he made pancakes, which I was delighted about, as these really were his speciality. He however, had always eaten something earlier. I was vegetarian and he was a big meat eater. I would notice my caravan smelling of cooked fatty meat some days. The cloying sensation stuck in my throat and it angered me, then I would feel ashamed of my selfish feelings.

He bought a new television, much bigger than my portable. I didn't know what to say. I was not happy because I loved my own space and didn't want a big TV. I hardly watched anything preferring always to read or listen to music. Now I had to endure the sound of a television constantly on in a small space, and him laughing out loud at some comedy. He would leave little gifts lying around, cheap perfume, DVDs, chocolate. This made me feel ungrateful, like a selfish miserable cow and I felt bad. I should be thankful…thankful to him for buying me things. What was wrong with me?

Whenever I wasn't with him, like at work or blessedly when he was out and I'd have my caravan to myself, I planned on telling him to leave. We could still see each other but he had moved in too fast. I didn't want to live with him and had not asked him to move in. I could see that he had invaded my space, and like Japanese knotweed, was slowly taking over. I didn't want this but when I was back in his company I failed to express what I felt and blamed myself for being miserable and moody. I was also beginning to feel lonely, and where before I'd always been happy in my own company, I was now beginning to rely on his.

He had a particular boyishness about him and talked about life in the south of France. He came from a good family and had worked as a model in his younger days. He was tall with great bone structure, dark hair and mysterious eyes, but at first I didn't believe him. He showed me photos. A tall, handsome, cosmopolitan man with thick black hair falling over his face stared dreamily at me through an eighties camera lens. One shot he claimed had been for a Marlboro's cigarette advert. A black and white image showed his bare torso, jeans fashionably hanging on his hips, one arm raised to take hold of a half burned cigarette. An inch of ash trapped forever on film just before it fell.

He was different to the Northern lads where what you saw is what you got. They could be crass and insensitive in comparison. He had an elegance that set him apart from other men. He was not the young model in the photos anymore but still carried an air of sophistication that I found myself becoming more and more attracted to. One evening, after a particularly tiresome day, one of the lads approached saying I had a treat waiting at the caravan. Joel had built a decking around it and was sitting in a chair waiting for me, a cold beer ready. What I didn't know then was that he hadn't paid for the wood. When my boss told me Camelot had been billed for it, he denied this and put it down to a simple misunderstanding. I believed him and was cross at my boss for thinking otherwise.

The most frequent conversations Joel concentrated on were how he had grown up with horses, and he talked a lot about his classically trained stallion. He claimed he'd been successful at show jumping and dressage competitions. Uncannily, anything I showed an interest in, he loved too. We were obviously meant to be together. I was slowly being swept off my feet into a world of falsehood. I should have known, recognised the clues, but instead I was about to learn the biggest lesson of my life.

"She won't let me see my child," was another story. "If I buy him anything she refuses to give it to him, so there's no point in me trying." He had a four-year-old son with his ex, a child he pretended to love but because he claimed his ex was so mean he wasn't allowed to see him. He would feign distress at this, making me feel sorry for him and want to help him. Now I can see that she wasn't any of the things he accused her of being. He didn't try to see his kid because he didn't care. Trolls have no feelings or empathy towards others. They feed off others' hurt and pain instead whilst hiding behind a mask of false selflessness. Financially he was in trouble too, because he inherently believed he could just take money and do what he wanted. He didn't think about paying people back.

Joel had been born near St. Tropez on the Côte d'Azur. He told me his parents owned about a hundred acres of land. He was going to go back to France to live with them, as they were very elderly, and run a business there. He wanted me to go with him. I could bring my horses and I could set up my own trail riding business. After my experience in Portugal I knew I'd do a damn good job of it. All I needed was a base with lots of land to keep horses in an idyllic location. It wasn't going to be just any old trail centre. I would run exclusive adventure rides and offer classical riding lessons too. Wynnie and Caramello would be so happy, and I would be happy, my ambitious wishes coming true, no longer just a fantasy. Foolishly I allowed myself to dream and succumbed to temptation.

Hell

Sometime during the day, they moved me to the infamous cata-combs that lay below the Grande Tribunal de Justice in Nice. I was handcuffed again and brought before a judge. With a trans-lator present I was asked to confirm my name and that I had indeed lived at the address in Brittany. "Yes," I stammered, my throat dry with fear. I was feeling even more confused and wanted to scratch my back as I felt the sweat trickling between my shoul-der blades, but the handcuffs prevented this simple relief. I tried to ask what I had done wrong but was shouted at. "Silence!" The policewoman glared at me. How dare I question the judge?

My confirmation of name and address apparently meant I was guilty and was to wait in the cells for a transfer to the women's prison. They even took my bra away (in case I hanged myself) and simply abandoned me in a stinking stone cell. Ammonia stung the back of my nose and the putrid stench of vomit and faeces coated the air. In a trembling voice I pleaded to be allowed to phone the British Embassy and my family, but I was denied everything, and still had no idea what I had done. Thank God Susan had taken Tessa. I dreaded to think what would have happened if she'd have fallen into the hands of French social services.

Loneliness crept over me, settling upon my shoulders like a coarse heavy blanket of desolation.

"Hey, Engleesh girl, do you have cigarette for me?" A sly, heavily accented voice sliced through my whimpering. I was not alone, yet the alien voice offered little comfort. With panic thumping at my temples, I retreated to the corner of my cell and concentrated on silencing my breaths as the voice continued its idle taunting. As the fear wolves closed in either side of me baring their teeth, a voice in my head sung… *hello darkness my old friend.* I ran deep inside myself to a country garden with sweet smelling flowers. Here I sat and attempted to calm my breath and hold the darkness at bay.

To the Dark Tower I came: A Thorn Hedge of Lies

Oh how I dreamed, and I am embarrassed to say I went with him for all the wrong reasons. I allowed myself to be taken in by lies. Joel had a particular carefree flair. People liked him, warmed to him and relaxed around him. I grew to genuinely trust him even though my intuition kept rearing her ugly head and telling me I shouldn't. I denied her and got angry at her for spoiling my fun, and soon I *was* having fun. He would drive me anywhere I wished to go. When my friend and I wanted to go to the cinema or to watch a show in Manchester, he would drive us and pick us up after. He would be always smiling and never got irritated or annoyed. He seemed completely selfless, eager to do anything to make me happy.

"Do you want an aperitif?" he asked me on our first meal together. I giggled, feeling a bit of a philistine because I didn't really know what constituted an aperitif.

"I don't know . . . are you having one?" I didn't want him to notice my ignorance.

"I don't drink and I'm driving," he said, "but I suppose a little aperitif can't hurt." I blushed, feeling silly, realising that of course he didn't drink, ever, and always drove.

"I'll have whatever you have, because to be honest I've never had an aperitif before. It's not something us Welsh are familiar with. I usually have a pint of ale," I replied, deciding to be upfront and not try to be something I wasn't.

"Well in France I used to enjoy a kir," he told me. "A blend of cassis and red wine, or sometimes a pastis maybe, my father's favourite." I wasn't sure what cassis was and certainly hadn't a clue about pastis so I nodded, wondering if this English restaurant could offer such delicacies. "But there is not much choice here," he continued, studying the menu. I noticed his hair had grown and now brushed his shoulders. He wore black rimmed glasses which added to his sophisticated *Europeanness*, his olive skin making him look decidedly Mediterranean and deliciously French. "How about a Martini Rosso?" He looked up at me expectantly.

"Whatever you say," I replied, a dreamy smile plastered over my face as I relished this cosmopolitan gentleman's exquisite company.

I listened as he chatted about medieval Provençal villages near his home where delightful little restaurants, that served only the best food and wines, were frequented by the rich and famous. He promised we'd visit these places, and not forgetting the mesmerising Côte d'Azur beaches where I could swim in a cerulean paradise hardly more than half an hour from where we would live. He talked animatedly and with fondness about his childhood home. I understood and realised why he was so keen to leave the dreary North West of England and felt honoured he'd asked me to go with him. Through that final busy season at Camelot we began to plan our future.

Firstly, he told me, there would be no money until we got to France and I would need to fund the journey. I dutifully went to the bank and took out an £8,000 loan. By this time I trusted Joel and had made my decision. I was going with him to France and taking my horses. I was earning a good wage, and my reasons for such a substantial loan – to buy a new performance horse for my work – was accepted by the bank. Then with my (the bank's) money we bought a horse trailer to transport Wynnie and all our stuff. Joel had a Land Rover Discovery which would pull this to France. Caramello would follow with transporters.

I'd never had a bank loan before, nor owed money to anyone either. I lived within my means and worked hard for every penny. Anxiety came knocking in the early hours as my first experience of money pressures and fear of debt crawled insect-like into my dreams. Intuition began rearing her head again and shouted at me, calling me an idiot. Angrily I shushed her and smothered her warnings in Joel's reassuring words. He promised he would begin work straight away on arrival in France to make the repayments.

The horsey business would take time to set up so he would take over financially and I should not worry. I suppressed my anxieties and reassured myself that he knew what he was doing, there was no way he would have talked me into a loan that we couldn't pay back. He laughed at my concerns and I began to believe everything would be okay. I trusted him and relaxed into his confident embrace. He would keep us safe.

The journey over to France was surreal. I wasn't present in my head. I'm not sure where I was but I was a long way from me, if that makes any sense. Life with Joel had raced onwards to new pastures leaving my thinking, worrying self behind, and I didn't want her to catch up. I feared what she may have to say about my reckless decision. I kept myself ahead of reason so I didn't have to respond to any sensible questions or doubts. We stopped by my parents' house briefly before continuing on to Plymouth and taking the ferry to France.

I introduced Joel to my parents. They were polite and he enchanted them with long descriptions of what life was going to be like in the south of France. They seemed to trust him and what he said otherwise I'm certain they would have tried to stop me from going. I wish they had, but then I was always head-strong and I was now a grown woman. They were probably relieved to see the back of me and genuinely believed I was in good hands. *At last she's finally going to grow up and settle down,* was what they probably thought.

In their eyes a tall, friendly, confident young man had fallen in love with their daughter. He wanted to take her to his substantial property in the South of France where I would live a life of luxury and they could come on holiday. He told them of the full-size swimming pool and uninterrupted views over the Gulf of St. Tropez. I'm not sure my Mum had had many thoughts about St Tropez before, but her eyes glazed over and the glamour took hold. What mother wouldn't be pleased for their daughter?

I remember speaking with her, having a mother-daughter moment and asking if she thought I was doing the right thing. "Do you love him?" she asked. "I don't know," I replied. And I didn't know. I was so very confused. I must love him or surely I wouldn't be going with him? I didn't tell them about the bank loan, and that I was funding this endeavour with the bank's money. Shame forbade me and I fidgeted in its thorny grip and silenced intuition before she could state the obvious. Had I confessed to my mother about the loan, I doubt she would have been happy.

Before we could leave British shores I had to pick up a few things from Martin's house. A friend of ours had died in a tragic accident. Martin was devastated and I should have been too. I should have told Joel to get lost and kept my horses, my trailer and my stuff with me and stayed home. I should have been there for Martin and my other friends. I should have stayed.

I was extremely apprehensive visiting Martin; he was a genuine person and I wasn't sure who I had become. He spoke of his feelings, but I hardly heard what he told me. It was like listening to something through white noise – like watching a programme on a TV with bad reception. I couldn't hear or think straight. Deep down I realised I was making a mistake but was too frozen to do anything to stop. Joel had spoken over any doubts and fears I had, telling me it would all be fine, that I worried too much, and I wished so very much to be happy. I wanted to flee my old life.

We said goodbye, and left for the ferry and the future. After a spell of sea sickness on the ferry and more travel sickness en route I developed an irrational fear that we would crash and be eaten by wolves as we wound through the bleak and unyielding Massif Central region. Unfortunately the Millau Viaduct – a huge cable-stayed bridge and the tallest in the world – was still under construction, which meant we took the old road through the Tarn Gorge.

My unease was not an over-reaction. Joel was a fast driver, even in the dark, and I was not used to such frightening landscapes. I was terrified for Wynnie in the trailer swaying around the treacherous bends, and wolves were not just a figment of my imagination – there are wolves in those hills. It is a volcanic mountain range consisting of huge displaced sections of the earth's crust that had been tortured into highland peaks and plateaus three billion years ago. Not only do wolves roam the dark wildwoods of Scots pine, but one of Europe's largest birds, the griffon vulture, soars through the otherworldly skies seeking carrion.

Hunkering down in my seat I pulled my woolly hat over my eyes to hide the scowling faces that peered from the trees and rocks. This land is steeped in myth and folklore, and creatures of legend sensed my foreignness. Joel laughed, saying I was missing some impressive scenery even if it was dark. I didn't care; I could feel something primal, a deep fear of the unknown. It was into this wilderness that I was headed, and I was not the one in control.

We stopped to check on Wynnie and top up his hay and offer him water. Ever such the brave little knight, he tucked into his haynet, breath steaming, whilst all around us dryads drifted through the dark trees. A secret world of hidden fey swarmed with strange goblins, fairies and elves peering and jostling to get a better look at these strange and lonely travellers. I buried my face into his mane and breathed deeply of horse; he nudged me, searching for mints which he crunched up with his hay. The soft golden smell of dried meadow grass and peppermint wafted into my senses giving me strength.

Sooner than I ever expected the hellish journey was over, and we were in the South of France, greeted by the warm Mediterranean autumn sun. Wynnie had travelled like a star, obligingly getting on and off the trailer to stretch his legs and graze in the large picnic areas along the roadsides. He was my soul mate and would follow me anywhere. I just hoped that I hadn't let him down, so I told him a beautiful green prairie awaited him. Caramello would be following in a couple of weeks, a welcome respite from Camelot.

Joel's parents had a lovely traditionally built, higgledy piggledy Provençal villa. Pale honey stone and a burnt orange terracotta tiled roof contrasted with quaint sage green wooden doors and shutters that blinked invitingly open. A large outdoor terrace wrapped around the back with uninterrupted views to the Gulf of St. Tropez. The azure Mediterranean Sea twinkled in the distance, luxury yachts dotted about like paper boats placed carefully on a theatre stage as the smiling sun beamed down. Steps led from the terrace to a full-sized crystal blue swimming pool and pretty little pool house. There were red azaleas, white roses and dark pink bougainvilleas growing in abundance, their sweet scent potently heady in the warm air. It was beautiful and I allowed myself to relax believing I had done the right thing. This was no troll's house. This was a fairy tale villa.

His mother and father greeted us warmly. They were elderly and brown as berries from the southern sun, their eyes twinkling with love and happiness for each other. Both were very different from Joel, who towered over them. They didn't use the upstairs of the house so this had been put aside for us. The décor was dated but I didn't care, there was more than enough room for us. His mother was excited to see Wynnie and kissed and cuddled him. There was a small paddock close to the house which had no grass but I had plenty of hay so I promised him the next day he could go out into the big fields. Joel's father was polite and offered us a glass of wine to celebrate our safe arrival. They were truly lovely people; having both had important jobs in Paris before retiring they had adapted to the Provençal way of life with ease. They'd spent many happy years holidaying here whilst they built the house. They were true pioneers and nothing like their son.

Although I had fallen in love with the house my main interest was in the land so I could set up a riding business. Horses needed grass and they were my first priority. Unfortunately, Joel's family didn't own a hundred acres like he had claimed. They barely had about four in total. Most of this was dense forest on very sloping land, not horse grazing at all. Why didn't I fly out first and check this out? Well I did. We went out for a long weekend. At the bottom of his property are wide open fields, these are what he said belonged to him. There were horses in these fields that he said belonged to his neighbour and they'd used the land since he had been away but he would sort it when we moved over. His neighbour would take his horses back to his own land. I nodded as I foolishly envisioned my horses galloping through the green fields with the vineyards in the background. In reality Joel had lied. That entire lovely open prairie belonged to his neighbour.

My dream of a trail riding and classical riding centre was not going to happen. There was barely enough land suitable for Caramello and Wynnie let alone any more horses. Joel didn't tell me this straight away though. He kept me waiting and daily asking why the neighbour's horses were still on the land. Caramello had now arrived and we only had two small grassless paddocks. We had to source more hay and feed pretty quickly or they were going to lose weight.

Then one day I confronted Joel saying we needed that land and enough was enough. I only had a small amount left of the bank loan and I needed to set up the business, which in such a magnificent area, I was convinced would be a huge success. That's when he dropped the bombshell. He did it in a way that made it all my fault. Somehow it was my fault that he had lied about owning the land.

"Look, it's not my land, okay, so stop going on about it. When I was young I always used the land, it may as well have been mine."

"But it's not yours?" I asked, still confused.

"No. How was I to know they would be using their land now, and not allow me to use it? I've been away for years. It's only because of you that I've come back."

"Right. So why say something is yours when it's not? Why would you do that?"

"I didn't realise it wasn't mine to use anymore. Will you stop having a go at me? I'm upset about this too, you know."

"So you said you had about a hundred hectares – that's over two hundred acres! Where is that land?"

"It's the forest, and I meant to say acres."

"Show me," I demanded, thinking that even a hundred acres of cork forest was still land where horse could roam and forage. We walked the perimeter. The land totalled roughly three hectares of sloping woodland. He'd believed it to be so much more when he was younger. There was still room and land for Caramello and Wynnie, which was more than I had; I should be grateful that he and his parents were willing to put me and my horses up. Tragically, I ended up using the rest of the loan to make the repayments and feed us, before declaring myself bankrupt. There was no money left to invest in any business – it had dripped out of the account at alarming speed.

Needless to say it had all begun to go terribly wrong. Joel was not my fairytale prince – far from it. He was a Troll and very experienced at using a form of glamour to entrance his victims. Behind the tall, floppy haired, smiling French man was a calculating creature, a creature that took pleasure from controlling others.

Joel was incapable of seeing my side of anything and truly didn't comprehend my hurt. He even seemed confused that I had believed the land to have been his. It could have been his, but it wasn't now because his neighbour had it. It was simple, and I should stop moaning and complaining and be thankful for what I had, for the opportunity he had given me. Poor him, being stuck with an ungrateful woman like me. Where was my recognition of everything he had done for me?

I was worrying about nothing, according to him. What was the problem about the loan and owing money? I didn't have to pay it back. He told me it would be fine, they'd scarcely come looking for me in France, it was under ten grand. I was hardly a big fish and soon it would be forgotten about; as long as I didn't return to the UK all would be well. Why not just enjoy ourselves? We'd fence off some more of the wooded area and there was enough room for Wynnie and Caramello. He would set up his business in construction and all would be fine, even his ex-business partner in the UK was going to be joining him.

His ex-business partner arrived to check the place out. Joel had promised him the delights of St Tropez and the chance to make lots of money. I discovered he'd promised him his own apartment – which turned out to be Joel's father's workshop that housed sleeping accommodation for guests. This is where Don stayed for a couple of months. Don was suspicious and seemed astonished that our home in France actually existed.

I confided in Don about the lie regarding the land and he was not surprised. He informed me that he was only here out of nosiness. He'd not believed a word of what Joel told him. He gave me a warning, telling me to get out while I still could because nothing Joel did was honest. He'd laughed, saying Joel wasn't even a good builder and had more complaints than success stories. He was a proper cowboy and had had to leave the UK due to the amount of money he owed and people who were pissed at him. He seemed surprised that I hadn't worked out what Joel was yet.

Don had no intentions of staying and soon headed home. I envied him. I spoke with Joel, telling him what Don had told me. He appeared to be genuinely upset that his friend would speak about him like that. He honestly didn't understand it, he was hurt and I actually felt sorry for him and cross at Don for having told me these unkind things. I was also frightened; I didn't know who to believe. I knew he'd lied to me about the land but could I overlook that? Wasn't the lifestyle here in the South of France with someone I believed cared for me worth my forgiveness? Was he Joel the man I had fallen in love with or was he the Troll, a creature I should run away from before it was too late?

Fortunately I met a couple of good friends, who recognised straight away what Joel was. "Make sure you don't get pregnant," Susan told me. I found that particularly odd as I had no intentions of having children at this time in my life – especially not with Joel. The glamour had ceased to work its magic and I too had begun to see him for his true nature. I drank quite a lot of wine to keep blotting out the truth; I didn't want him to be the Troll. I wanted him to be Joel. I was still smitten with my surroundings yet I knew it was all wrong, like a mist I couldn't quite see through. And it was easier to ignore what was happening to me when I was steeped in wine.

I yearned to leave, unable to forgive the lies. I needed to get away but believed my bridges to have been burnt. I owed money and had none, and when I spoke on the phone to my mother she didn't seem to want to listen about it all going wrong, and I didn't have the heart to spoil the delusion. I was also deeply embarrassed at my own stupidity for taking out a loan in the first place. Had I really been that desperate for love? Or was I just a shallow cow? A French accent and the lure of a fairy tale palace had ensnared me, hook line and sinker.

These thoughts bumped around in my head as my mum enjoyed telling me how the neighbours, who holidayed in the South of France, were amazed that I now lived there – complete with a swimming pool. I realised I had to make this work, I couldn't admit to my folly. Surely it wasn't that bad? The South of France was a beautiful place with a wealth of nature. Wild tortoise roamed the forests and bristly black boar played in the vineyards stealing the precious grapes. In springtime the air was filled with the sweet smell of mimosa trees, yellow flower puffs lining the driveway and tracks, their scent dizzying. I realise now that I had begun to grieve. I was grieving for Joel. The Joel I loved hadn't existed in reality, and the disguise had been tossed aside by the Troll. Joel was dead to me now, and I missed him.

I refused to allow myself to think about the fact that the Troll didn't have any money, other than what he took off his parents. He was French and in his own territory, yet he refused to find work, plunging us further into debt. With my bridges smouldering and all routes home unobtainable, I decided to throw myself into living there. Amongst all this beauty how could life be bad? If I tried hard enough I could ignore all the red flags. Drinking wine and swimming in your own swimming pool was a luxury I'd never experienced before. I could cope with this, surely?

I began to get some work as a *Spectacle* rider. This is quite a thing in France, referred to as *Spectacle equestre*, a theatre performance with horses, similar to what I'd done at Camelot but much less tacky. I had the costumes and the horse, Wynnie. I began to give a few lessons locally. There was enough land to keep my two horses and we fenced an extra paddock and field shelter where I was able to get a horse and pony on livery to make more money. No grass or open fields, but still they had some space and the Troll dressed up a lean-to to make a couple of stables for my horses. I felt I should be grateful.

I began to realise the Troll wasn't very good at anything; Don had been right. He set up another company but he was extremely lazy and didn't like to work so he ended up owing money to builder's merchants almost immediately – so much for helping me to pay off my UK debt. He could have been a success if he had been willing to try and not rack up so many unpaid bills. I honestly have no idea where he spent his money. He hadn't a clue how to earn an honest buck.

Meanwhile, I'd found a kitten. Mr. Woody was the most intelligent and delightful little cat you could ever want. Mowgli soon followed and now I knew I wouldn't be able to go home, because I loved those cats. So I stayed and tried. I worked hard looking after the horses in the desperate heat and drank away my money fears in cheap rosé wine from the local co-operative. Life could have been worse. I needed to count my blessings. Except I couldn't shake a tiny voice I kept ignoring that screamed at me to get away.

Hellfire and brimstone

Then as my first roasting summer rolled languidly towards the end of August, fire arrived. Some of the worst forest fires seen in the South of France raged through the landscape. I remember feeding the horses in the morning and seeing a sky full of birds all flying towards the coast. There was an eerie feeling in the air. The Troll went out and when he came back he informed me there was a forest fire nearby.

The rest of the day was spent frantically preparing for the worst. We were told to evacuate if possible but with animals and the Troll's elderly mother and father, who wasn't very well, this would not be easy. I had a thoroughbred horse on livery and a pony as well as my two horses, one of which was Caramello. Frantically I wracked my brains as to where they could go to survive the fire. So we brought them into the house. Caramello was sliding about on the dining room parquet flooring and munching on hay and straw. I'd brought as much fodder as I could into the house to keep them quiet. The Troll's mother was great and didn't complain about a thing. She was a genuinely good person and would do anything to help and this was a matter of life or death. She was familiar with the area and forest fire so was well aware of the risk.

Every container possible was filled with water. Every towel was dunked in the water and laid behind the closed shutters around the windows and doors to dampen the house. The whole house we began hosing with water in the hope it wouldn't burn. All the outdoor pool furniture was thrown into the pool. The large gas bottles that fed the cooker were also disconnected and thrown into the pool. It resembled a post-apocalyptic holiday resort. The sky darkened with thick black smoke; the sun was eclipsed by the red-hot glow of ferocious flames roaring through the countryside heading our way. The heat was immense, even breathing was painful. We wrapped sodden tea towels around our hot, smoke-blackened faces and waited.

Susan had run from her apartment as it would have been foolish for her to stay there alone. She should have gone to somewhere safer but she came to us instead to help, complete with her cat that joined our cats locked upstairs. So did an English friend who ran a bar in the town with his wife; he couldn't get back there as the fire had cut him off so he had to stay. Soon darkness came and the sound of the planes that were constantly dowsing the flames stopped as they could not fly in the dark. The night was black and red. It felt like being inside a furnace at a blacksmith's forge, or even Hell itself. Terrifying explosions sounded in the hills where gas bottles still hooked up to the villas blew up like bombs.

I was frightened, terrified mainly for my animals. I remember touching Caramello's neck and trying to reassure him but he knew my words were weak. He remained calm though, all the horses did. I suppose they trusted I would keep them safe. I believe they would have followed me to Hell and back, and me them. I checked on Wynnie and gave him an apple. Immediately he bit into the juicy flesh his teeth grinning at me, happiness in his eyes. Wynnie, my brave little painted clown, never failed to make me smile, even at times of disaster.

There were many deaths during that fire. I hope the arsonists that started them realised the damage they'd caused. When it reached us it came up the track towards the property sounding like a huge engine belching out fire and brimstone. The Troll's mother even walked outside exclaiming "*Le pompier arrive*" with a big smile on her face. She thought the noise was a fire truck come to rescue us but it was the terrible roar of the flames she could hear. We all fought the fire with hose pipes but when the electricity wires burnt the pump stopped pumping and the water stopped, dribbling to a slow piss.

The phone lines went down as the fire burnt through them, destroying the telegraph poles too. There was no one to call for help anyway, all emergency services were out and doing their best. I had an old mobile phone and noticed a tiny network bar. I don't know why but I phoned my old friend Jinx in Wales. I told him I may not survive but to tell everyone I loved them. I remember the crazy nutter laughing, probably stoned and not knowing the truth of my situation. Tears rolled down my blackened cheeks – tears for the land, the wild animals, and my animals and for everyone, including my stupid self, who longed to return to what I knew and where I felt safe. Then my phone died.

Four firemen died in the tracks not far from the house that night. It could have been more, but luckily for us and for them, a fire truck did eventually arrive. It was stuck; they couldn't go back because of a fallen tree. The truck was empty of water so the men had abandoned it and donned their suits and masks to escape on foot. I remember being outside throwing a bucket of water from the pool over the land around the house. We'd tried pumping the water out of the pool with a pump and small generator, but the hose pipes were bursting apart leaving only a tiny dribble coming out of the end. As I turned to head back for more water I fell on my arse in fright.

Coming up the hill was a cyberman from *Doctor Who*. Not only did we have a fire to fight but an alien invasion too? The cybermen have struck fear into my heart ever since I was a child. They were always the most terrifying of *Doctor Who* monsters for me, so maybe in a time of such fear my brain saw a cyberman instead of a fireman. I quickly realised my mistake as he took off his breathing apparatus. They were relieved to see we had a swimming pool and brought their truck up through the burning forest. This wasn't easy as the track was blocked by burning debris. They had to drive off the usual track and pass through a vineyard. The vineyards don't burn and it was hiding amongst these that many wild boars found a safe haven.

The firemen quickly used their pump to fill the truck from our pool and soon their professional hoses were spouting water. We were surrounded in flames but thankfully the hoses and the force of the water held them back, eventually quenching them. The rest of the flames moved away, heading through the forest, leaving the house and all the contents, including the living ones, safe. The firemen were amazed to see the horses in the house and even took a photo of Caramello in the dining room, a crystal lamp swinging above his head.

The surrounding land remained blackened and burnt for months afterwards. The smell of ash from the charred scorched land filled your nostrils and I felt dirty every day. The paddock electric fencing needed rebuilding before the horses could go back out so in total they remained nearly three days in the house. It was an exhausting effort to clean the house and get it back to normal. I did most of this with the Troll's mother. The Troll made excuses that he had other people to help, that he was an expert on fire and that people needed him. The truth of it was, he just wanted to talk a load of crap to them and then cash in on the poor unfortunates that had had property damaged by fire by charging them silly prices for fire advice. He was no expert; if the fire truck hadn't arrived we'd have been done for.

That was when another little cat came into my life – one with slightly burnt and blackened paws. The neighbours called him Flame but I named him Phoenix.

The Immaculate Conception

Having a baby abroad was not something I had planned. I was never very maternal, unless it was a baby animal I was dealing with. The feeling of a new life stirring inside me changed all of this. I didn't realise at first. I suppose to me it was like an immaculate conception. I had stopped sleeping with the Troll. I didn't want to go near him. I was bitter and could not forgive him for the lies. I blamed him now ultimately for my entrapment in a foreign land. Instead of getting my head straight and going home with my horses, no matter the debt, I lied to myself, saying things like, "It's better the devil you know" and, "At least the weather is good here".

I hadn't realised how much of my life I had left to live, and I was wasting precious moments being on the wrong track completely. I had this lesson to learn but I kept avoiding it. Instead of facing up to the truth, I buried my head in wine and tried to make out on the surface how good I felt. I believe it is on one of these evenings, when I was completely comatose, passed out on vino, that I got pregnant. I cannot to this day remember having sex with the Troll at this time.

I foolishly thought I may be having an early menopause at thirty-four. I was that disinterested in my body I thought and hoped my fertile years were over. I was having hot sweats in the night and weeping uncontrollably. I had an extreme concern for the cats. I was terrified something bad may happen to them. I wanted to protect them with my life. I panicked if I heard a dog bark, fearing it would come and kill them. I was terrified of the sound of the hunters' guns that could be heard in the distance as they shot at wild boar. I thought they would shoot my cats and I became highly agitated and anxious. I was riding quite a lot at this time, which helped to keep my nerves under control. I would regularly perform at a Bodega, where people would sit and have meals whilst horses and riders in Spanish costumes danced to music like the Gypsy Kings. Caramello was great at this. He loved to be admired and it allowed me to dream I was someone else.

I should have been feeling happy. I'd made my bed and was well and truly lying in it, doing my best to get on with life, but I was very depressed during the New Year celebrations. I had been working at the Bodega. I angrily recall myself smoking too, and drinking lots. I wanted to go home. I had an overwhelming urge to see my friends and family, my depression was immensely dark, I was racked with sobs and an abnormal fear of everything. In February I got a cheap flight home alone, my first visit since moving. It was extremely emotional. My breasts had become larger and still it didn't dawn on me. I thought it was weight I was putting on as I was menopausal. I hadn't had a period recently but had definitely had one since I last, consciously, slept with the Troll as that had been ages ago, or so I thought.

I was visiting a good friend, Joanne, back in Wales, with Elaine. As I sat in her house I told them how I was feeling and that I thought I was going through the menopause. She had not long had a baby herself. She looked at me stupidly and told me to go upstairs and that there was a pregnancy tester in the cupboard in the bathroom and that I should bloody well pee on it. I tried telling them I'd not had sex for a long time, but hadn't really confessed how disastrous my life abroad was. I was foolish and everyone thought I was so lucky to be living in the South of France and how they wished they were me. I should have said, "No, it's crap, I need to come home and I need help to bring my horses home, I'm trapped." Instead I smiled and said nothing.

For the first time in years I turned my attention to my insides. As I walked up her steep carpeted stairs, so different to the terracotta tiled staircases of the South of France, I felt a tiny spark illuminate. I remember being frightened as I had no idea how this could have happened. I got to the bathroom and peed on the stick. I stared aghast as it indicated that I was pregnant. My mind was whirling. I told my friends the news and they were over the moon for me. I wasn't. I was terrified. In hindsight I should never have returned but should have arranged for my horses to come home. I should have left my cats for the Troll's mother, as rabies vaccines were too difficult at this time to contemplate and the quarantine was ridiculous. The horses, however, would have been easy to arrange to bring back. I just needed to open my damn mouth and tell people how miserable I was and ask for help, but I also knew I couldn't just leave my cats, I loved them.

So I said nothing. I remember crying before going back and my mother asking me what was wrong. I didn't tell her I was pregnant. I didn't tell my family. I just cried and told her I was cold, as I was cold, very cold and extremely weak. I curled up into a ball with my arms around my precious cargo and wept. I couldn't believe I was having a baby and some part of me still didn't believe it as the conception date was odd. When I boarded the aeroplane I remember carefully placing the seatbelt over my stomach and stroking it. "I'll keep you safe somehow," I whispered.

Back in France the Troll took the news as a matter of fact and a doctor later confirmed it. At the doctor's – his – they conversed in French as if I was invisible. I'd picked up a lot of the language but this rapid dialogue interspersed with raucous laughter was impossible to follow. "Wait!" I said. "When is it due?" I was told in October. "But doesn't that mean it was conceived – when? January?"

"Oui Madame," said the Doctor. I looked at my ex. "But we haven't had sex since last summer and I've had periods since, and I always have heavy periods." He just ignored me and talked over me, in his loud dominating French, translating what I said and laughing, except he didn't translate exactly what I said. The doctor looked at me. "Eh, there is sometimes possible to bleed a little when pregnant and it er, no problem." He smiled and he and the Troll proceeded to sign me up for my first scan date. Nobody was interested in what I had to say.

My Birth

My mother has told me many times the story of my own birth. Apparently, straight after I was born the nurses put me, naked and screaming, in – what my mother called – a turkey dish. I was left for about an hour. She had been abandoned too; her feet were still in the stirrups on the birthing table. A kindly nurse eventually popped her head around the door and sorted us out; there had been an emergency and apparently we had been forgotten about. I know that the time spent alone when I was born contributed greatly to how I have lived my life. A yearning for solitude combined with a desperate search for companionship led to insecure relationship choices.

I try to remember how it must have felt when I was left screaming in that turkey dish, devoid of all contact. It was me, so somewhere in my psyche is the memory of it, and this must be the same for everyone, yet what must be my earliest memory seems to have been turned to a recurring dream. During this dream I feel entirely alone. I don't know if I am cold or hot as I feel nothing physical, except a vast expanse of nothingness and all-encompassing isolation. I see nothing; it's not blackness but more of a yellowy light, like twilight when the sun is going down. Slowly I realise I can hear something which is outside of the rushing and pounding sensations inside my head. It gets louder and more distinct and I begin to tune out of the internal white noise and instead reach for this new sensation, my ears eager to absorb the euphony.

The sound is rich and full, a range of tempos pitching and blending, moving all around me and I have no idea for how long I simply absorb this new wondrous experience. A separate presence cuts through my solitude, both frightening and relieving, which stimulates my new-found senses. Warm air glides over my face and my skin tingles. It's immensely comforting and I reach out, eager for more.

My fingers encounter their first sensation of touch as they brush against something soft and velvety. Instinctively my eyes focus through the golden light. A blurred shape fogs my vision and slowly I notice it's covered in tiny hairs that glint like sunbeams. The warm air comes again and the hairs flicker as I find myself staring at the oyster pink skin of a horse's muzzle. Looking up I see a pearl coloured horse nuzzling me as if I was her foal. Her eyes are the colour of pale weather lit with the flickering of distant storms and all around fly a concerto of songbirds. She still visits me, when the darkness becomes too much.

One day at school when I was about seven the teacher read us a Welsh story from the *Mabinogion*. This is a collection of ancient tales written in medieval Welsh from around the twelfth and thirteenth centuries, although the origins are much older. They are myths and legends full of heroic deeds of the Celtic people and feature King Arthur. I sat next to my friend and eagerly waited for the other children to stop fidgeting so the teacher could begin the tale of Pwyll, the King of Dyfed, of when he first encounters Rhiannon the Goddess of horses and birds and falls in love with her.

Inside my head the ancient Celts came to life. The Goddess Rhiannon appeared like a vision resurfacing in my mind. She rode a glowing white horse lit with a golden light and was surrounded in tweeting and chirruping songbirds. I wanted to cry out, I've seen her! I know her horse, it comforts me when I'm alone. I was too shy to say this out loud but a familiar sense of recognition flashed through me. I realised it was the magical Welsh Goddess Rhiannon who had visited me. She hadn't spoken to me, had not even acknowledged me herself but her horse had, and that meant everything to me. The glowing pearl coloured horse with oyster pink skin holding the weather in its eyes had visited me and comforted me when I had been terribly alone and left its imprint on my soul.

It's strange how childhood memories still weave their magic somehow, shaping and directing our journey through life. Are they just our young imaginations running wild, a form of intuition, or our inner child trying to remind us of an alternative reality we've long forgotten? Maybe they're something else entirely. We may all have been imprinted by something that hides deep in our psyche. For some this becomes their saviour, for others a way back into a nightmare.

Hell

Whilst waiting in that stinking cell to be transferred to the prison I prayed to the horse with the weather in its eyes and remembered holding Tessa in my arms for the first time. Slowly I began to rock back and forth, now oblivious to the filth. I could almost feel her warm body held tight against me. I started to hum very slowly the Christmas carol 'Little Donkey' which I used to sing to her whilst stroking my thumb between her eyebrows. I'd struggled during those first months of motherhood. I could never get that time back again, but I wanted to.

I had been so unhappy and depressed yet wanting to enjoy my baby.

I should have been surrounded by friends and family, enjoying the ups and even the downs, except I felt lost, isolated and alone. I hated him for what he had done but I had done it to myself, I had allowed him to manipulate me and trap me in a rural idyll where I felt I should always be grateful to him. How could I claim to be so unhappy when on the outside I appeared to have so much?

I was still Tessa's mother though. I had escaped him with her once and he hadn't bothered us for years. They couldn't lock me up and take her from me. She was starting secondary school in September. I'd hidden her uniform so she couldn't find it and dirty it trying it on too many times before school. I began to panic thinking I'd not see her on her first day at the comprehensive school and she would not be able to find her uniform.

"Let me out!" I screamed. "I need to go home, you don't understand. My daughter is starting secondary school. I have to be there." I pummelled the bars bruising my wrists, but nobody came.

Birth of Innocence

I had an easy pregnancy. Being fit helped. I didn't crave for anything except porridge. The temperature in the South of France was blisteringly hot and there was me making a breakfast of warm steamy porridge every morning. It was quite idyllic on the surface. I'd feed my horses and even continued to ride in my spectacle up until I was over six months. I trusted Caramello and Wynnie; they understood I was carrying a new life. They would nuzzle my stomach and take deep inhalations absorbing my smell. The flies, however, were terrible. Whilst carrying the hay and feed I'd have to keep stamping my legs to get rid of the horseflies. They were huge. Caramello had a terrible reaction to them one day. The vet had to give him an emergency antihistamine injection. I tried fly rugs and strong chemical fly sprays but nothing really worked.

After finishing with the morning work I'd be drenched in sweat and fly bites so couldn't wait to strip off and jump straight into the swimming pool holding my pregnant bump. This lifestyle was wonderful and a couple of friends came to visit and thought I was living the high life. This made it even more difficult to express the awful truth about what was really going on underneath. The Troll was supposed to be running his own business but it went from bad to worse. I knew we had money worries but I had no idea to what extent.

I met a good friend at this time, who I'm still in contact with. She was the local post mistress. She lived locally and loved horses. In return for riding lessons, especially classical dressage, she helped me look after my horses. She would be able to carry on taking care of them when I went to the hospital to give birth. Caramello was such a tyrant but she was good and not a threat so he accepted her. One day though his inner beast broke free and he attacked her in the paddock. She managed to get away but he did hurt her. I don't think she quite believed me when I'd warned her that he could suddenly change and become something dark, something evil and completely different to his usual self. She certainly believed me after this.

The idea of giving birth was beginning to frighten me. I'd been to a few post-natal classes held in French but didn't feel prepared. I was feeling very lonely. I wanted my old friends and family. I didn't want to do this alone in a foreign country. I didn't feel close to the Troll, I had seen his true colours and there was a part of me screaming, *What are you doing? Get out of this situation. The biggest thing that can ever happen is about to happen.* I was going to have a baby and I was lost, confused and depressed. Instead of dealing with it I withdrew. I spent more and more time just sitting with my horses or lying on the bed where it was cool, cuddling the cats and crying into their fur. I wanted to leave so badly but these animals were my friends. How could I leave them?

The morning of my labour I felt something was distinctly wrong. I told the Troll something was up. I couldn't feel any movement inside anymore, the tiny shiftings and fidgetings of a little creature inside me which I'd become accustomed to, had stopped.

"I can't feel her moving," I said. "Something feels wrong." He looked at me over his breakfast, a huge bowl of coffee in which he dipped a whole baguette smothered in jam.

"It's nothing," he said, because he knew everything, you see. Everything that happened he knew about it, and even though he had never given birth, he still knew far more about it than me.

"I'm telling you something isn't right," I shouted. He tutted and said he'd take me in to the hospital when he'd finished eating. I waited tearfully in the car. At the hospital they reassured me there was nothing wrong. All I could hear was his booming voice talking to the nurses who smiled and giggled with him, agreeing that I was an over sensitive, erratic foreigner. I felt like I was being treated like a child. Nobody was hearing me. They told me that my baby was fine and she would not be born for another two weeks and that I should just go home and relax. At the petrol station on the way home we bumped into Rose, an Irish lady I'd come to know and like. She took one look at me and told me I'd be having my baby later that day and I should go back to the hospital. I could do nothing but smile and explain what the capable nurses had told me.

The Troll dumped me at the house and drove off. I was now alone in a house at the end of a two-kilometre track on the edge of the Massif des Maures. The Troll's mother was away visiting a friend in Paris. His father had sadly died not long after the fires. This had left the Troll with a free rein to undo all the neatly organised work to the property his father had originally done. His father had been neat, efficient and reliable, the opposite to his son. His mother knew this but because he was her big overgrown cuddly Troll she always made excuses for him. They would argue horribly though, with her shrieking like a banshee, all to do with money and his inability to make any. Even to this day she constantly financially bails him out of trouble. She knows what he is and I think deep down feels responsible. I've never understood why she cut her soon-to-be-born granddaughter out of her life.

I went inside the pretty Provence style house and tried to relax. The cats came and sat with me glancing up unnervingly every few minutes. My contractions had started. At first I told myself it was nothing, probably just those Braxton Hicks people go on about. My waters hadn't burst so I just kept wandering from the bedroom to the kitchen. It was a sweltering autumn day; the summer was showing no signs of leaving. At around 5pm I decided to feed the horses whilst I still could. Unfortunately Sylvie, the post mistress, wasn't around on this particular day either.

I waddled outside and carried a large net of hay and bucket of feed down to Caramello's paddock which was at the bottom of a steep hill. Halfway down I had to drop everything and fall to my knees. I had a huge contraction which left me breathless. I got up and still thought it must be normal as they'd told me I wasn't having the baby today. I was going to phone the Troll but didn't want to hear his voice going on at me and telling me how wrong I was and to get a grip and stop being such a stupid woman. I made it to Caramello and sat down awkwardly next to his hay and feed. He sniffed at me and nuzzled me with food all over his mouth. He seemed more interested in me than normal and kept stopping to eat to look thoughtfully at me.

There were strange sounds coming from the wall of trees that bordered the paddock. My ears strained to hear what I thought was a wolf howling but was probably only a dog in the distance. I'm sure I could hear grunting and stamping too; there were wild boar that used to come right up close to the house. They unnerved me, huge bulky animals that I never quite trusted. Sometimes they looked harmless and friendly and then other times they would leap out in front of the car headlights snorting, challenging you with eyes glowing, beings from the underworld. I imagined the smell of blood drawing them out of the forest. They were hunted here and probably hated humans, even vegetarians like me. Would they show me any sympathy? Caramello would protect me, of this I was sure.

I began to cry and I really felt a bit like Mary, thinking not only can I not remember the conception but this baby is going to be born in a stable too. Another contraction got me back up and heading for the house. I was frightened now. I looked nervously at the forest. I was unfamiliar with this land. The legends and folktales were different from my own. I didn't recognise the spirits here, and they were here, I could sense them. I'd left Caramello's paddock and felt exposed, like someone or something was watching me. The cats were at my side with worried expressions. They knew something was up. Next I fed Wynnie and even he stopped eating to nudge at me. His dark eyes, that I have known since he was a foal, looked knowingly into mine with a hint of concern. I sat with him, feeling safe as the contractions eased a little as the cats rubbed against me. This temporary lull didn't fool me though; my baby was on her way.

I made it slowly back to the house and began to time my contractions. I had been told they would be spaced apart and would gradually get closer together. First maybe fifteen minutes apart then gradually getting less, but mine were all over the place. I'd be fine for half an hour then they would come very fast and close together and then far apart again. I tried to phone the Troll but there was no answer, so I told myself to wait. The baby was fine and probably not coming today, it was just my imagination. I had been in the hospital that morning and this is what the professionals had told me.

I eventually heard the Troll arrive. He did not come to find me to check I was all right but lit the outdoor grill and selected himself a nice frozen steak and placed that on to cook. I staggered downstairs clutching my huge belly and through gritted teeth told him I had to go to the hospital.

"No you don't," he said, matter of fact. "I took you this morning because you were playing stupid and they have told you that the baby is not due yet." Playing stupid? The very sound of his patronising French accent made me want to commit violence against him. I struggled to explain that I was having contractions and that they were all over the place.

"Well the baby isn't coming then," he said, very matter of fact. "The contractions need to be regular distances apart; if not then they're not proper contractions." He said all this whilst staring at the glistening hunk of dead animal sizzling on the grill, prodding it now and again as the fat oozed out, dripping onto the hungry flames. "Have you eaten anything today?" he asked. "Because you've probably got a hunger pain. I'll cut you up some melon and bring it up in a bit if you like."

So that was that, I had a hunger pain and had to eat melon. I turned to go back upstairs and had one of the largest contractions that day. It left me on my knees, sweating with gritted teeth struggling to catch my breath. This thankfully triggered him to phone the hospital at least. I could hear him laughing again and making out that I was exaggerating and that I was being silly. Then it dawned on me that his voice was becoming more serious and that he was talking in English not French. He came over to me looking a bit miffed. He hadn't had the response from the person on the other end that he wanted. They obviously didn't agree with him and they were English.

"Here," he said, stroppily handing me the phone. "The midwife is English so you can talk to her." My relief was overwhelming. I clutched the phone like it was my one and only lifeline. "Hello?" my voice quivered.

"Hello, I'm the midwife on tonight. Can you explain exactly how you're feeling please?" A warm hearty northern accent reached out of the phone like a friendly gentle hug. Through tears and shortness of breath due to contractions I started explaining. She interrupted me. "How far from the hospital are you, my lovely?"

"About 25 minutes away if we're driving fast," I replied.

"Get your bag and get your hubby to drive you in now, OK? Don't delay."

"Will you tell him please?" I asked. "And he's not my hubby, we're not married." I felt like I needed to disassociate myself. I handed him the phone and turned for the door. "Can you get me my bag please, it's ready." For the first time he began to look slightly worried and drove me to the hospital.

The jeep jolted over the ruts and bumps in the track. I had to sit on my knees with my hands on the headrest and ask him to stop twice. I wailed in agony, my voice alien. When we arrived he told me to stay put whilst he found out where to go, but I was already out of the door and heading towards the *Urgence* sign. There, thankfully, capable people surrounded me.

In France they always, as standard, administer an epidural. The anaesthetist was ready for me and although I feared this huge needle more than giving birth I allowed the professionals to do their job. "It OK now, you will have some time to relax whilst the epidural start to work, it takes time," they said. The lady doctor with whom I'd had my regular ante natal consultations arrived and went to check on my dilation. My waters still hadn't burst. The lovely English midwife held my hand and the Troll began fiddling with my epidural tube saying it wasn't working or something. Please get him away, I remember thinking.

The next minute the lady doctor tossed her long plait back and said, "La bébé descend." She had to break my waters with what looked like a large knitting needle. I was exhausted and felt bizarrely distant from everything, and the strange thing was I didn't scream. They were giving me oxygen and telling me to breathe and it all became rather frantic, except I felt like I was floating amidst bird song and drifting into a lithium sunset. The doctor took a scalpel to me and then brandished some terrifying medieval-looking forceps. They all struggled, urging me to breathe and to stay with them, that the baby needed me to push and to breathe because she needed oxygen.

After what felt like an age but was less than two hours the doctor finally placed a bloodied, slimy thing onto my stomach. My baby. My hands shook as I touched her. She looked at me. I'm not sure if that is my imagination or not but she looked straight at me and me her. The midwife was putting scissors into my hand and urging me to cut the cord. I struggled to hold them and needed help to close the scissors over the long, slippery, purple umbilical cord that had fed and nurtured her whilst safe inside my womb. Then she was lifted off me by the paediatrician and checked over. I could see him holding her up whilst she screamed at the indignity. "All is good," he told me, glancing over and grinning.

Whilst the doctor began stitching me back together, the Troll retired to my bedroom. In France the hospitals are very well equipped. This one was very new and extremely posh. I had my own room with ensuite bathroom and a television. A large window displayed a stunning view of reddening autumnal vine-yards and the Gulf of St Tropez. This is where the Troll had laid down on my bed with the TV on and gone to sleep. The midwife seemed rather annoyed and told me she had failed to wake him. They wanted to take me in soon but he was refusing to wake. I didn't really care. My stitching was finished and my baby was snuggling up and I had managed to breast feed her. So I slept on the delivery bed, my baby in my arms, whilst the nurses busied themselves tidying up.

The English midwife visited me often and I knew she was aware that things were not quite right between me and the Troll. I knew she didn't like him as she mentioned again that she had been shocked that he had gone to sleep on my bed and refused to move. She didn't believe him when he explained he was so deeply asleep he couldn't wake up when she tried to rouse him. I mean, what sort of man does that when his baby has just been born?

New Life

I suffered quite badly after the birth. My stitches hurt and I'd also dislocated my coccyx, which was agony. I stayed at the hospital for a week until my iron levels righted themselves and my beautiful innocent baby girl began feeding better. I was breast feeding and this delightful new little life I was responsible for didn't seem to like my milk. The nurse would come in to ask how many minutes she had fed for and I'd reply in hesitant French "Umm, two minutes on one breast and three on the other." Then the nurse would lapse into a long explanation that this was not enough and she should be about ten minutes on each breast.

Regardless, Tessa, my precious little life, was thriving in her tiny world. I was mesmerised every time I looked at her. I was no longer alone in this strange land, although I felt very lonely; I wanted family and friends to flock around me. Susan visited, and Rose, but I was mostly alone until I was well enough to go home, except it wasn't the home I wanted to return to. I'd prepared a beautiful nursery in the spare room and I couldn't wait to get out of the hospital, even if the idea of being responsible for this brand-new life felt quite terrifying. My friend Susan told me, "Look, you're great with animals, she's also a baby animal and she's all yours." This thought was overwhelmingly wonderful, yet also left me in a state of electrifying anxiety too.

The cats were so happy to see me; they wanted to peer into the carrycot at what I had. Later, we would go on picnics where I would push the pram and my sleeping baby into the forest and sit on a blanket breast feeding whilst the cats tucked into a tin of sardines. I attempted to connect with the natural world that surrounded me but it never seemed quite right. The landscape was beautiful, and when I first moved here I had been amazed to walk and ride into the countryside and see wild tortoise strolling around. I would pick them up to say hello and put them down again, always careful that the horse never stepped on them. After the fire I never saw any more.

My daughter Tessa was a beautiful baby, with thick dark curly hair like me, and I'd rub my thumb against the soft down of her eyebrows whilst humming her to sleep. She was elegant and didn't look like the usual chubby babies squished into bonnets. She would sleep well for a few hours but would wake demanding to feed. I slept in a bed with her in the nursery; the cats weren't allowed in overnight for safety reasons and I missed their warm furry bodies in bed. The Troll I did not miss. He didn't have much to do with Tessa as a baby, preferring to disappear off all day, allegedly making money but instead just getting into more debt.

I was exhausted and remember mucking out the paddocks with my shovel and barrow whilst wearing those cups on my breasts. I'd be sweating and the milk would be squirting, filling the cups until I'd feel it overflowing and I'd have to stop and open my feeding bra and tip the breast milk into the earth. Tessa would be sleeping in the pram with a fly net over her so she wouldn't get bitten by anything nasty. The winter was mild until the very depth of December and January, when we even had a light dusting of snow. I struggled to breast feed for the next few months as she still only took a tiny amount and fed often through the night, exhausting me. Then at Christmas time my mother and father visited.

I was happy and made a huge effort to decorate the house to create the Christmas of my childhood memories. I would cradle Tessa in my arms and show her the twinkling lights of the Christmas tree. By this time I was exasperated with the breast feeding and would pump my milk into little bottles because I had so much and she drank so little. My mother could really sympathise with me as my sister had been the same. It was wonderful to be able to talk to family and discuss baby matters and to finally have some help. Christmas day came and went and then my parents went home leaving me sinking further into my undiagnosed depression, now exacerbated by post-natal depression and tiredness.

I look back and wish these early months with my baby could have been different. I wanted to enjoy her but unfortunately it was blighted with depression. I had what was later described to me as situational depression: A dark cloud that had descended because I felt trapped by my circumstances. I didn't want to be with the Troll and I wanted my life back but now it was even harder for me to make my escape with a baby in tow.

I gave up with the breast feeding after getting an infection. The pain in my breasts was worse than giving birth or the dislocated coccyx, which I had to have put back twice in the rather embarrassing way of a chiropractor's finger up the bottom. My breasts were huge and rock hard and I had a fever. The doctor prescribed antibiotics and tablets to dry up the milk. Tessa would now have to make do with formula. She rejected pretty much everything. Eventually she was prescribed one that she accepted – but not one I could buy in the supermarket. It was an expensive formula that I could only get from the Pharmacia. At least she was drinking and putting on weight, although she remained a problem to feed pretty much up until she was about ten years old.

I began to ride again as my coccyx healed and some semblance of my old self returned. My friend Alison came over to stay for a couple of months to help me with Tessa. This was a blissful reprieve. It was so nice to have some help. Just having someone to take her from me and give her a bottle, especially in the morning if I had been up at night with her, was a godsend. Alison enjoyed herself and was great with Tessa; we relaxed by the pool and it was good to chat, although I still didn't confide the truth to her. I was happy on the outside but deep down I knew Alison would go home and I would have to stay. Even though it was a beautiful place the foundation of my whole life here was built on shifting sands and like The Tower in the Tarot, it would come tumbling down.

Darkness descends

This section of my life could have been a fresh start, had I left, but I descended deeper and deeper into darkness. The Troll had got himself into so much debt we were having people call round to the house demanding money. These were workers that worked for him (because he was too lazy to do any manual work himself) but then he failed to pay them. Some were, I discovered to my horror, illegal immigrants from North Africa. This, the Troll assured me, was why they'd never go to the authorities to demand their payment. I was mortified. I hated these people wandering about the place too. Not that I have anything against them, but they treated his father's previously immaculate workshop like a tip. Rubbish was thrown all over the place. The Troll was slovenly, and now he had a group of slovenly helpers that were soon to become very angry indeed.

On one occasion a particularly irate worker knocked at the door. "Don't answer it!" yelled the Troll running upstairs. "Why?" I replied eyeing the door nervously. My post mistress friend Sylvie was with me. Tessa was asleep in her pram. The knocking resumed, turning into urgent pounding and yelling.

"Open this door now!! You owe me my money!! I work for you and you no pay!!"

The Troll descended the stairs with a bag. He was leaving for the UK. "Tell him I'm not here but will pay him later." At that he ran out the back way of the house, past the swimming pool, through the undergrowth and down to his car waiting below where he drove to the airport and left. Sylvie and I were very frightened. We knew the person demanding payment had been wronged by the Troll. I approached the door. "He's not here, he's in the UK," I said.

"You lie!!" came the immediate reply. "I see him run into the house before." I sighed and said he'd gone again and I was so sorry. The voice got angrier. "Open the door or I will burn this place down with you and your new baby inside!!" Sylvie and I clutched each other. "Don't be silly," we pleaded. "It's not our fault – please, be sensible." How ridiculous that we should be pleading with this person. Then he must have heard the Land Rover engine because he took off down the track. This sort of thing began happening all the time. I was afraid to go outside. I was afraid for my horses that were living in their paddocks. I was afraid for the cats. I was afraid for my poor little baby girl and for my useless self.

Another time Sylvie and I called the police. The Troll had allowed a man to live in his father's old workshop. This man had a gun. One evening I heard gunshots. I investigated and found his girlfriend crying. "He is crazy," she said. "He will kill me if I don't go now." Then glancing back fearfully she got in her car and left. I looked around only to find him, and the source of the shots, by my horse paddocks staring up at the sky firing his gun. He turned to me laughing and pointed it at me. I froze. Some part of me didn't register that this was actually happening. It all seemed so surreal. I noticed he had a fierce looking dog at his side. Then I heard my cats that had followed me as they always did. This place was supposed to be a safe haven, an idyllic place for a new mother and baby where we went on pussycat picnics.

"Does the dog chase cats?" I said stupidly, trying to usher the cats into a tree.

"What?" he said, the gun still wavering in my direction. "They bloody kill them!" he laughed, buckling over.

"Then please take it away and leave too," I said, trying to stay calm and not make an unstable situation worse, although in truth I was so bewildered and dazed I thought I was hallucinating.

"I'm not fucking leaving! I can stay here as long as I like! Your partner tell me I can. You can't do anything."

"I can," I said. "I'm going to phone the police if you don't put that gun down."

"The police? They will not help you. I will kill you first." He proceeded to walk towards me pointing the gun straight at me. "Your partner tell me I can stay and stay I will. My dog too and if he kill your cats then he have good sport." His spittle showed white on his lips, his eyes sparkled with insanity. I could smell the alcohol on him. "Your partner care nothing for you, he think you a joke." He laughed as he relished my fear. I realised that this was a very serious situation. Why had the Troll told him he could stay? I remember disagreeing to it in the first place, but the Troll never discussed anything with me and didn't care about my opinion or safety. He probably had him there to keep the others away – a larger devil to scare the smaller ones.

I turned and ran towards the house praying I wouldn't feel the sharp pain of a bullet in my back or the black numbness of a shot to the head. I hoped the cats were following me and the dog was not. I ran through the trees and heard a shot; I tensed as I ran but no bullets caught me. Sylvie was at the door waiting for me. The cats were wrapped around her legs. All cats have a strange way of being able to teleport when needed. Sometimes they step into fairyland and back out again looking very smug and full of pixie dust. I wished I could do the same.

"What's that idiot doing?" said Sylvie. "I saw his girlfriend leave, what were those gunshots?"

"He's threatened me with a gun, and he's got a big dog," I replied as I grabbed the phone. "We need to call the police." My voice cracked and I started sobbing. "He said he's going to kill us. I'm so frightened for Tessa." I was racked with uncontrollable weeping. Not just normal crying which can be a release, but a sort of keening noise that just got worse, increasing my tension. I began to wring my hands and for the first time understood the saying. What would he do to Tessa if he killed me and Sylvie? Sylvie phoned the police.

The Gendarmerie arrived in three cars; they appeared to know something we didn't. They were prepared for a dangerous criminal. Sylvie was told to stay in the house with a female police officer and I was put in the back of a car with another female police officer. She questioned me where I had seen him, as the car drove slowly following my directions down the track towards the workshop. There he was! He turned and prepared to point the gun at the police, like a scene from the movies. They leapt out of their cars using the doors as cover as they pointed their weapons at him. There was a lot of shouting in French of which I understood nothing. The female police officer pushed my head down into the back seat for cover so that I couldn't see anything. Then it was over.

They took him away and he spat at me as he passed. Sylvie and I gave statements and later we discovered he was on the run from the police for the attempted murder of a police officer. So the Troll was harbouring a serious criminal to scare away lesser criminals whilst leaving the country once again. Not once did he ever give a thought to my safety or that of my baby girl. I don't refer to her as his; she is mine. He had nothing to do with her. Later, when the police had left, I watched her sleeping. Her head rested to the side with her two arms up in the 'don't shoot' position that all young babies sleep in. How ironic I thought. Something had to be done. I had to leave... but how?

I remember telling this story to my parents on the phone. They didn't seem to believe me. My mother told me to stay where I was, I couldn't come home, how silly of me to think it. My tales of devils threatening to burn the house down and police taking a wanted criminal, who had pointed a gun at my head, away in the night all seemed too far-fetched. I don't think they listened. I remember yelling and crying on the phone, my distress obvious to all but them. The Troll also spoke to them I believe, and acted like I was hysterical and over-reacting as usual. A stupid woman 'playing stupid,' as he often described me. The fact that Sylvie was a witness and supported what I said seemed irrelevant.

This was the first time I would feel completely out of control of my destiny. There would be no help from home. They had been hoodwinked by the Troll. Nobody believed me. I was a mess, suffering from both long-standing depression and post-natal depression. If it was Victorian days I'd have been locked up for a bad case of female hysteria. Later, he actually threatened me with this and it struck fear into my heart. I'd always thought of trolls as liars or clumsy dirty creatures, bad, but not evil. I was wrong; this troll was rotten to the core. "I am French," he would say to me. "You are crazy; I can get you sectioned if I want. Nobody will believe anything you say. You are hysterical." I remember becoming quiet. My emotional outbursts, my sheer desperate cries for help, were falling on deaf ears. He had no mercy for me.

Trapped in the Dark Tower

"My mother has decided to sell the house," announced the Troll one day. "We can have our share and move away and do our own thing." This was a big move. The house had been built by his late father; this place had been special to his parents. Why couldn't he make a business work? We had no mortgage. I was making a little money with the horses as well as looking after Tessa. He could very easily have made a good living doing ground maintenance and gardening. Instead he called his company a construction company and got into huge debt buying diggers and tipper lorries and large vans because he had to have them. Now he had to pay it all back, so the house had to go.

I know this must have hurt his mother but to be honest, I didn't care about her anymore. The screaming arguments between her and the Troll were driving my already unstable mind further into depression. Then again, maybe this was my chance to leave. With a shudder I remember he talked me into looking at properties for sale in America. I shiver in fear at the thought of having ended up so far away, but I couldn't think straight. He blamed his mother saying it was all her fault and if we got away from her then it would all be all right. The house was valued at a little over 1.6 million euros. It sold to the local Countess for 1.5 million. It didn't stay on the market for long. She only bought it as it bordered her property and she had been after it for quite some time. She didn't get involved in the deed herself, being far too much of an aristocrat to get involved with such peasants as us. An American woman arranged the whole sale.

The money was divided three ways. The Troll's mother had plenty to buy another smaller home, his brother had his share and the Troll had his, of which a chunk had to go towards paying off his ridiculous debts. Nevertheless, I believed this could be a new start. We now had something we hadn't previously had, unless you count my eight grand, but we now had money in the pot to begin with. I should have demanded he repay me my money and got my horses and child out of there, giving the cats to his mother. I attempted to suggest it but realised he would rather kill me than help me financially to leave him. This money was his and he made it clear to me, very matter of factly, that I would have nothing if I left; he didn't care if I loved him or not. I realised leaving him would not be as easy as I thought.

I began carefully suggesting we return to the UK. This was the most practical option in my opinion. I could work more easily in the UK, we had enough money to buy somewhere that had land where we could put up some stables and do horse livery, and I could offer classical riding lessons. Livery pays well in the UK; people are always looking for reliable yards to stable their horses. I was trained and qualified to do this and for the first time since I was a young girl, my dream of having my own yard looked hopeful once again. I began to remember who I was and where I had come from.

Unfortunately for me the Troll was too clever. He knew I would be amongst friends and family in the UK. He would not be able to get away with the way he treated me here. I had rights and he wouldn't be able to threaten, frighten and bully me with garbage about the French system. He opted instead for Brittany. Property was very cheap there. He could buy a farm with triple the acreage of what could be bought in the UK for the same price. He was now looking forward to bragging about being a land-owning farmer to a new group of people, somewhere he wasn't known. Somewhere he could begin his bullshit, exploiting and ripping people off all over again.

Much later Sylvie informed me that she had spoken to people in the South. They told her the Troll had had to run from his home town originally because he had pissed so many people off they wanted to kill him. Now, many years later, he ran from there again for the same reasons. How had I and my lovely horses – and now my beautiful baby girl – got so trapped in a poisonous bed of treachery? One thing I did do was to start looking into transporting cats to the UK. The rabies laws were going to be relaxed for pets. They would need to be vaccinated against the disease six months previous to leaving. I decided to sort this out, just in case.

The Troll purchased a beautiful little farm in central Brittany with about 33 acres. I must say I fell in love with it to begin with. The house was a traditional Breton longhouse with a country cottage garden, an idyllic place for Tessa to grow up, and closer in mileage to the UK, making me feel slightly safer. Realistically speaking I should have known it would all go wrong. The Troll spoke of us getting a farming grant from the EU. The business would have to be in my name because horses came under farming in France and to be eligible for this you had to have a qualification in your chosen discipline. I was the one with the qualification, so into my name it went.

I needed more stables and an outdoor school to give lessons and to train in. I also needed another schoolmaster horse, one who would take some of the spectacle workload from Caramello who was well into his twenties. Wynnie was my best lesson horse but he wasn't very tall so I was limited. We set out to buy a new horse and got completely ripped off. I was not ready for such a corrupt market. People in the UK think the horse market is unscrupulous, but it has nothing on France. There are some good, honest people out there but you need to shop around. Anyway, I did not want to buy two horses but the Troll, with his addiction to spending, bought two from a notorious dealer. Both were unsuitable for my needs.

One we had to exchange because he was insane even by Caramello's standards. The replacement was a terrified nervous Spanish type that had a huge scar on his underside, probably the result of the bull ring. He needed lots of training and reassuring. It wasn't until much later that I was able to use him for lessons. The other was a youngster, that later on became a great lesson horse, but he needed an awful lot of schooling first. I train classically and correctly, I don't rush horses, I allow them to progress in their own time, not mine. Neither of these horses are with me anymore. I wish things could have been different, that I could have saved them all.

Meanwhile the Troll had to get a job or do something. He didn't. He was in fact unemployable. Instead, he decided to take over the business that was in my name and make it his own. It remained in my name but he took control. I was exhausted looking after a young child and a yard of horses. We had a couple of liveries at this point too. They didn't bring in the money they would if we had been in the UK but it was something. I physically couldn't do anymore. He had to try and earn some money. So he began trying to make hay to sell but he didn't have a clue how to do this. It didn't work, so we had to pay contractors to cut our grass to feed our own horses, instead of buying it in. We also owned a small wood. The only heating in the house was log burners. We had to buy wood in because the Troll was far too lazy to cut any and ended up giving it to the neighbour who worked hard cutting it and thankfully gave us some.

He seemed to be busy doing nothing, nothing the whole day through. Then with money from the bank he bought a big horse lorry and decided to put livestock transport on the business too. Soon we were in debt again. I hadn't even noticed this happening. He would confuse me with forms that were written in French and shout at me if I questioned anything he asked me to sign. Debt collectors began to come to the house. They threatened to take the horses if we didn't pay. An unpleasant little man slithered over to me when I was in the car pulling out of the drive to fetch Tessa from nursery. He began to yell that the Troll owed him money. He said he was a Gypsy and would take the horses to slaughter if he didn't get paid. He then spat in my face. Already the nightmare had begun again, but I didn't have Sylvie or Susan this time for support.

I was now even more trapped than I had ever been. I had found three new-born kittens on the main road that everyone was ignoring. They were terrified of the traffic. Tessa spotted them. "Mummy!" she said pointing, her face lit up. "Little cats." I gathered them into my coat and took them home. They were frozen with fear. Now I had even more little lives to be responsible for and to worry about. I spent so much of my time taking care of the horses, the cats and Tessa that I hardly had any time for me. I had become lost again. Every time my own feelings began to surface, I panicked. The reality of my situation was too much to deal with, mentally and emotionally.

Every day I feared a knock on the door and the letters that

came though the post. I would take Tessa to nursery then see to the horses before hiding in my room, on the floor with my hands over my ears, rocking back and forth. The Troll was away doing his 'livestock transport' and getting into more and more debt. He would disappear for weeks at a time. Sometimes I would not have any money to pay the bills and the electricity was cut off. The food in the freezer was destroyed and I would sit at night by candle-light. That's when the wolves would come, their shadows springing across the walls. I'd try not to look at them, but I could feel their hot breath on my neck. I'd drink more cheap wine in order to blank it all into darkness.

Tessa had a little battery operated mushroom nightlight, and in these dark times I would go into her room. It was the only place where the darkness could not fully reach. She was safe, the cats would all curl up on her bed and it was like a beacon calling me away from the evil that stalked me. I'd not wake her and when my sobs became too loud and strangled I'd have to return to my ghoulish candle-lit room where I'd drift into an uneasy sleep and the same dream would plague me.

I was astride a dark bay horse facing the biggest storm I had ever faced. The noise was deafening, wind goblins the source. I could barely work out where I was, as the wind lashed the horse's mane into my stinging eyes. Wasteland surrounded me, cold and desolate. I would begin struggling to do something, but would always awaken before I knew what and the dream would fade leaving nothing but a dark sense of unease. The candle burning low – shadows closing in on me – blowing it out and in complete darkness, I'd curl up in my bed and wish for oblivion.

Ironically I would have days when I would wish for another baby. Not that I wanted one with the Troll, but on my fortieth birthday I remember crying so hard because my chances of ever having a baby again back home surrounded by people I loved and who loved me, were disappearing. I hated the Troll for ruining my experience of being a mother and having a baby. The birth and her first years had been blighted by fear and anguish.

I wanted to be happy; I wanted to have a normal life like other women did. I wanted to have a baby and have people visit me and love me and I wanted to enjoy the experience. I know this is different for everyone, but my terrible situation didn't help. In a fit of madness I ended up paying fifty euros I didn't have for Spider, a tiny Siamese kitten I encountered. He needed lots of love and attention and, being Siamese, was very demanding and not independent like other cats. He became my new baby. I treated him like a tiny new-born and he responded like one.

I would never sleep with the Troll again. I warned him one night not to ever touch me or he would regret it. I don't know what I would have done but he didn't attempt anything anymore. He probably had someone else. He spent longer and longer away from home. This left me very lonely, though I had Hannah, a young girl that had started work experience with me. She was English but her parents lived in France. She was too young to understand my pain but later became a very good friend and realised what I'd been through. Tessa, the cats and the horses kept me sane, they were my life. We also had two dogs; they were his dogs though. I loved them because they were animals, but they lived outside in the barn, cuddled up in the warm bales of hay. I always thought they were watching me, making sure I didn't go anywhere or do anything he would not approve of. I saw them as his spies. Silly I know, as they really were just a goofy pair of dogs and great guards too, for which I was grateful.

Then the Troll announced that we would have to sell the house. The debt wasn't great enough for the bank to take it, but we would have to sell and pay it off. He told me the debt was around forty thousand euros. In reality it was worth eighty. The thing was, this debt was now in my name, because my name was the one on the business. He proceeded to arrange meetings to discuss repayments with debt collectors and would be asking me to sign various forms. These forms were all in French and I signed every one. I should have questioned but whenever I did, he would begin shouting and yelling at me and stressing me out so much that I would experience shortness of breath and what I later discovered were panic attacks.

I contemplated suicide and believed Tessa would be far better off without me. Everyone would. If I ceased to exist then wouldn't all the pain and suffering cease to exist too? Would it all just stop if I stopped – if my life stopped? I began to obsess about how to end my life. Would it hurt? I'd need to do a proper job because I did not want to wake up in hospital and face the nightmare all over again – and this time it would be worse. He would be able to tell people I was insane and have me sectioned. I would be considered unsound of mind and Tessa would be taken from me. If I was to die then I needed to stay dead. Then one night a white horse came to me in my dreams.

It was where I had got the story from that I related to Hannah one evening. I believe it was Caramello, but a future dead Caramello who had come back in spirit to give me the strength to carry on. I had climbed onto his bare back; he was warm and the sun was setting over the greenwood. He carried me through the trees where I saw myself as a little girl galloping past on Smokey. My eyes were closed but there was no mistaking the huge smile on my face. Behind fluttered some colourful paper horses. A red one stopped, reared, waving its forelegs at me, his inky black mane billowing around his head. I laughed, urging Caramello into a canter to follow.

We glided behind my child self until I began to recognise the track. The weather had turned colder but not unpleasantly so. I could see the familiar Welsh mountains I loved so much. I followed the track as it led down to the old mine I had found so enticing, not far from the dwarf lord's castle. There I watched as two kids took shelter from a wild Welsh rainstorm. They were not bothered as they laughed and giggled. I recognised the other child as Donna, one of my childhood riding friends, and we were sharing a bag of fun size Mars Bars she had brought from home. I remembered the day and could almost taste the sugary sweetness replenishing my sugar reserves.

Slowly the image faded and the feel of Caramello's back became the sheets of the bed I lay in. He had reminded me of who I was and where I had come from and I decided there and then that I would find my way home. Somehow, I would get home again and ride on those same tracks. I would take Tessa home so she could grow up next to the Welsh mountains and live a happy, normal childhood, something I knew she would never get from the Troll.

The Troll took over all aspects of the sale of the house. I had become quite compliant. I knew I could do nothing until the debt was paid and my name was clear. I began measuring time in tea bags. Whenever I refilled the tea caddy, I would wonder if we would have sold by the time it was empty again. Eventually, after a painful five years of stress, we sold to a private buyer. They had responded to an ad the Troll had placed on the internet. This left me wondering, *Where to now?* The Troll still refused to go to the UK. He knew I'd leave him the minute my feet touched familiar soil. In a fit of weakness I pleaded with him to give me enough money to get home, to take my own horses and make a proper home for Tessa. I had fallen to my knees at his feet and literally begged him.

The Troll refused. He told me I could go on my own if I wanted but I'd have no money from him and I would not be able to take Tessa with me. He was French and knew how the system worked, I wouldn't stand a chance. I was crying so hard his face blurred through the tears. My throat was choked and the frustration was pulling my mind to shreds. I just wanted to go home. He ignored me, his eyes shark-like and dry, not a flicker of emotion passing over his face.

"Look at the state of you," he said. "Nobody would leave someone as messed up and unstable as you to have full custody over their child." And he laughed. Laughed at how stupid I had been to even consider this.

My leaving was obviously out of the question, and so began the next ordeal, before I could finally escape, and escape I would… one day.

Hell

I was relieved when they eventually came to get me. A part of me still believed it had all been a misunderstanding and they would apologise to me and let me go. This thought disappeared at the sight of my jailers' stern faces. I asked for some water, for which they begrudgingly had to find a plastic cup as the tap next to the toilet was filthy. I hadn't been offered food and it was almost two days since I'd last eaten. The water was tepid but I drank it all, I was so dehydrated from the heat and the tears. Handcuffed, I was led through the corridors to the outside. Instinctively my eyes closed against the sharp rays, the hot sun burning me. I was an unholy demon, cowering from the daylight, before being pushed into a steel cage in the back of an armoured car.

Panic rising in my throat I battled with claustrophobia, as fear flooded my already exhausted system. After hearing the doors lock I began struggling mindlessly and with the use of sweat and a little blood as lubrication, ignoring the pain, I managed to slip out of my handcuffs. Escape! Yes! My adrenaline told me to flee when they opened the door again, but somehow reason and my own integrity kicked in and warned me against causing trouble. I was innocent of whatever it was they believed I'd done; so I sat in complete cognitive dissonance until the vehicle stopped. Suddenly, I bizarrely began to struggle to get my handcuffs on once more, forcing them back over my sore wrists so as not to anger my captors.

I had arrived at the prison. After a degrading strip-search I was led to a cell which I would share with another five women. Fear rose inside me – how could I possibly share a cell with hardened criminals? I'd never even had a parking ticket before, and here I was in a foreign country being wrongly locked up and labelled an international criminal. What would they do to me? Holding my hands tightly over my eyes I simply began to weep.

The jangling of keys stopped and with a faint creak the cell door opened. The guard spoke to the inmates in French before pushing me forwards and slamming the door behind me. I stood, my body shaking, tears squeezing through unseeing eyes into my palms. I stupidly hoped that they couldn't see me if I couldn't see them. I flinched as a hand brushed tenderly against my shoulder and a kind voice spoke soothingly to me in English and another few voices joined in. Prising my hands away from my face I cautiously looked at my companions.

I was in a cell with five other women. The walls were a sickly yellow, a window with bars hung open. The heat was sweltering and sweat dripped off us. I looked at the women and in their eyes I saw the first signs of compassion I had seen since my ill-fated arrival. I cried even harder and they hugged me. I hugged them; they were angels in a dark place. They realised I had not eaten for days as they too had suffered the starvation treatment. They rustled up an apple and a peach. I sat and struggled to eat the fruit, my jaw hurting and my stomach cramping.

As I ate they told me their names and where they were from. Ingrid was maybe in her thirties from Germany, Melani, a Russian, about late twenties with very long black hair. A shy girl who, like me, wouldn't stop crying introduced herself as Arla from Serbia but I could call her La La. Asara was maybe fifty, very much a mother figure, from Algeria, and then the youngest was eighteen year old Kinga from Hungary. They were all so beautiful. I introduced myself and they had never met anyone from Wales before. I told them it was a magical country but rained a lot. Asara gave me some water and held me whilst I cried some more.

I told them I hadn't done anything wrong and relayed my story of being arrested at the airport.

They were shocked at how I had been treated and were concerned for me and my daughter. Ingrid told me I would not be there long, that the police would realise there was a mistake. She was hopeful for me, although she had been awaiting trial for two years. There were delays, she said. I asked her what she had done, what any of them had done because none of them looked or behaved like criminals...but I'd never met a criminal in jail before. They glanced at each other, neither answering. Kinga broke the silence and in the carefree way of the young smiled and said they were not good girls. This I found hard to believe.

The prison guard returned with a flannel, toothbrush and paste, a prison nightdress and spare bedding for me. There was a toilet in the corner behind a shutter type door and a tiny sink to wash in. She informed the others in French that I would be leaving to fly to Brittany at five the next morning. They asked her why and she replied that I could be lucky; the judge there wanted to see me. Ingrid translated, reassuring me that the judge would see my innocence. They all agreed that I did not look like I should be in jail, but neither did they.

I was exhausted, but my anxiety levels were so high that sleep completely evaded me. The girls were talking quietly, and Ingrid told me the prison doctor gave out Imovane sleeping pills, as prison is not an easy place to sleep, and did I want one? They had a packet and I got the feeling those pills were like gold dust. I hesitated but was so tired I'd welcome any kind of oblivion. I told them I'd never taken pills but they assured me one would do no harm and could only help.

I trusted their advice and soon I was dreaming of pennies ceaselessly falling into a well – *down they went to the sound of silence. I began to fall too, slowly at first then gathering speed. Reaching with my hand I touched the nearest penny. It spun; the Queen's head smiled. Landing softly onto warm grass I watched the pennies float upwards turning into songbirds, fluting a concerto, and breathed in the sweet scent of horse. The pearl coloured mare had found me. Now I knew I'd be okay. Whatever happened next I would and could get through this.*

At four thirty I was awoken by the guard and told to get up to be taken to the airport and flown to Brittany. The girls wished me luck, each hugging me farewell. I was handcuffed again and my journey north began. I was going back to Brittany. I remembered leaving with the Troll all those years before. I had wanted to return to Wales so badly but was too afraid to do so. He had financial power over me and I believed he would do anything to make me suffer if I left.

Resolution through Wonderland: So Near and So Far

Soon I would find myself agreeing to travel even further away, finding myself even more isolated. Mental exhaustion had taken over, I couldn't think rationally anymore. I didn't know how to explain it to my family; they had high expectations of me. They thought I had fallen on my feet. I too had expectations of myself. I did not want to admit failure. I didn't want to embarrass my parents or myself. Coming home unmarried with a child, penniless, with a now eighty-thousand-pound debt hanging over me – that wasn't even mine – just wasn't acceptable. Was it not better to endure? Was I not lucky? I wasn't living on the streets. I wasn't living in a council flat being beaten to a pulp every night by a drunken husband with a string of kids to look after. I wasn't a junkie being battered by her pimp. This is what I associated with being abused. I didn't realise that what was happening to me was still relevant. It was still abuse.

The Troll wanted to go to Spain. I feigned interest. I spoke to Debbie one night on the phone. "You can't go there!" she said. She'd lived in Spain and had learnt the hard way it wasn't all it was cut out to be. She had put her place up for sale and was heading back to the UK.

"Where else can we go?" I asked. I wasn't interested in going anywhere other than home. I hadn't really confessed just how bad things had got to Debbie. The thought of moving again took my breath away. Panic danced on the periphery of my mind. I'd begun to experience panic attacks whilst shopping in the local supermarket. Sweat would pour down my back, cold and clammy as I feared the debit card would be refused. Even when I'd put money in I had no idea whether it was still there or if the Troll had spent it. This became a regular thing and I still didn't even realise that what I was experiencing were panic attacks. I thought it was me being stupid, something the Troll often said I was.

The Troll would promise when he was away on his many trips 'earning money doing horse transport' that he would put money in the bank, but he would use more than he made. He didn't even do a good job at the transport business. It was atrocious how he would leave horses on the lorry overnight standing in their own excrement. He was not a horse transporter in any sense of the word and I was embarrassed to be associated with him, but I couldn't get away. I was terrified I'd be responsible for paying the debt.

"How about Portugal?" said Debbie. "It'll be easier out there, you know the people, speak a little lingo and the land will look out for you." I believed her. Maybe Portugal wouldn't be so bad to return to. The thought of moving thousands of miles further away from my beloved Wales was daunting but somehow I had to find the strength. I was in the hands of fate now. I began looking for farms for sale on the internet so I could show the Troll. I was careful not to be too eager to move there or he may wonder why I wanted to. He wouldn't want me getting any kind of strength from anything. He needed to be in control.

He liked the idea of Portugal and decided to purchase a shabby pink derelict farmhouse. Our budget was so low we could only afford places in the bleakest, remotest parts. Eventually, we bought the pink house which was situated on the edge of the Gardhunha Mountains in central Portugal. This area was a national park and had its own ethereal beauty. It was an eerie expanse of rocky crags and boulders famous for UFO sightings.

I knew it was ill-fated from the start. When we viewed the property an old shepherd was sitting under the olive trees. He'd left a lot of litter strewn about, something the uneducated Portuguese in rural areas are frustratingly prone to doing. I noticed a dead sheep on the land away from the rest of the flock. It had been torn apart. The shepherd had a dog with him, eyeing us slyly. Then I spotted another dog tied by twine to a tree some way away. The dog was thin and panting; he had no water. A foreboding tentacle slithered over my spine and came to rest on my shoulder.

The Troll mentioned the dead sheep to the estate agents who were very obliging and arranged for it to be removed and the shepherd moved on as we wanted the grass for the horses. The land would now be ours as the Troll had decided to purchase. Later, after we had moved in, I went for a walk and there hidden on the edge of woodland was the rotting remains of a large black and tan dog – the dog I had seen tied to a tree. What shocked me the most was that a wooden stake had been plunged through the heart of the dog, pinning the carcass to the ground. The twine was twisted tight around the decaying strips of flesh and fur that was once the poor dog's neck.

I recoiled, stumbling over my feet. I retched, backing away. I heard the call of carrion crows overhead and felt their shadows pass over. I looked again, unwilling to believe my eyes, hoping they had lied and it was not a dog staked to the ground. This sort of cruelty to domestic animals was something I had never witnessed before. I had seen horrible things when I'd worked for nine months as a veterinary nurse, but these were injured dogs and cats that the vets struggled to save and they more often than not did. Animals could not be murdered in such a horrific way. I struggled to try to understand why this had happened, why would someone do this?

My conclusion was: the shepherd was obviously very poor. He didn't own a gun. The black and tan dog was probably his, a young one maybe. It was also probably starving. The dead sheep was likely to have been killed by it, and without a gun the shepherd had killed it with the stake. Like our farmers would shoot a dog for sheep worrying. This one was probably tied to the tree with no water in order to weaken it before the deed was done. Maybe the shepherd would have left it tied to starve and die of thirst had he not been forced to move on by our purchase of the property. Later I took a couple of my crystals, a rose quartz and an amethyst, over to the dog and placing them onto his wretched corpse I said a prayer for him and covered him in earth, after removing the hideous stake.

Moving was traumatic. The horses had to go to a French livery yard and the cats into a cattery before they could come. The Troll drove the lorry with our furniture and I drove a Toyota van towing a small trailer with more stuff. A friend drove the Land Rover and a horse trailer. (All these things newly purchased by the Troll with his handful of money from the house sale.) Now thankfully, I believed, all the money he owed had been paid back. Although in the back of my mind I knew it wouldn't be long before it all began again and I was right.

We had moved in the October and by February we were skint. I thought there had been at least fifty grand in the bank but the Troll had disappeared to England for weeks and weeks, returning with a new horse lorry, a huge digger and a trailer to carry it around with, and God knows what else he had spent the money on. Thankfully this time the estate agents had been on my side and advised me to put the house in my name if he was using his name to set up one of his new 'companies'. I was surprised, but after he thought silently and calculatingly the Troll agreed and put the house in my name. In fact, it was as if he had planned it all along.

The White Queen, my Saviour

A few months previous to the move my auntie died. I had been desperate to return home to visit her but didn't have the money. The Troll was away and I couldn't leave the animals. I remember feeling like the horses had become my jailers. The very animals that gave me strength, the very essence of my soul I now saw as my enemies. It was a terrible feeling, and being unable to even attend the funeral left me devastated. The Troll seemed not to care. I regretted not seeing her before she died, because I loved her so much. She was my father's sister and had never had children of her own and since I was a tiny child I had adored her wit and company.

In a Wonderland I no longer recognised she became my White Queen. She had left me some money. Shallow as it sounds, this was everything to me. It meant I could possibly get away. I was a prisoner plotting my escape. I was stuck in Bluebeard's keep, but now I had a key. Slowly Portugal began to become the familiar Wonderland I had once experienced. Hannah, my friend and past work experience student, came out to stay with me. Having her help with the horses and Tessa was a blessing. She disliked the Troll and didn't trust him either, so in her I had an ally.

Our nearest neighbours were English. I couldn't believe how fortunate this was. Soon we became good friends and straight away they saw exactly what the Troll was. Now I had friends and allies. They repeatedly assured me that I wasn't mad, and they helped me to understand that there was a way out. With Hannah to look after the horses and cats while I was away I was able to organise a trip home for Tessa and myself. I needed to open a bank account in which to place the money I'd been left. My previous debt had now disappeared as so much time had lapsed and I'd declared myself bankrupt all those years ago. I booked a cheap flight and off we went.

It wasn't quite what I expected. My parents were older than I remembered them. They were clearly unsure about me coming home. They still couldn't see, or didn't want to see, what the

Troll was. I believe they didn't particularly like him – none of my family did. Since then, they have confided that they thought him a braggart and a liar, irresponsible with money. My mother confessed to hearing him shouting on the phone in French to his own mother, when he was in the UK on one of his infamous transport business trips. He sounded like he was demanding money, the words *carte de credit* featuring in the conversation. He then asked my parents to lend him £100 because his mother had stopped her card, which he was using. My mother gave him the money.

However they felt about him or about my leaving him, I don't think they were ready to welcome me and everything that came with me into their arms. I was a grown woman with a child and horses; living with them was not going to be an an option. The words *You bloomin' sledge* taunted me, and I feared I'd let them down. I was a disappointment. I'd failed once again to grasp the mug. I looked around for places to rent with land, realising the horses couldn't come back to the paddock and stables I had used as a child. My life had moved on. My father now mowed it with a ride-on lawn mower; it was like a bowling green.

One day, like a blow to the head, my father told me that he believed I was making a big mistake coming home. My daughter was not familiar with English schools or Welsh ones. In his old-fashioned, no-nonsense, quite harsh way, to which he was sometimes prone, he informed me that Tessa would most likely grow up a dunce if I came home, having never been to school in the UK. They hadn't a clue about anything I had been through or was going through. I had kept most stuff hidden, being unable to speak about things, so I really couldn't blame them. My mother also told me that the house was now in my name and I should use the money to make it a nice family home for Tessa and me. Needless to say I returned to Portugal completely and utterly deflated, but also determined to give it one last go, maybe eventually manage to grasp that enamel mug.

That was when the darkness closed in again. The Troll was now aware I had some money because I'd told him I wanted to build decent stables for the horses and make one last try at my horsey business and making the house a home. Unfortunately for me, he talked me into withdrawing lots of cash and giving it to him, because he was going to build the stables. Oh, and the electric and internet had been cut off while I had been away 'holidaying' with my family so I would also have to pay that. The money slowly began to dwindle out of my account and into his pocket. No new stables appeared and the new windows for the house failed to materialise too.

Two Mad Hatters Visit

The Troll was away again, had been gone for weeks, doing his transport business where he got people to forward him the money for jobs and then failed to do the jobs. This was how he ripped off loads of French people, because he no longer had a French address or business. His business was Portuguese based and I had paid the two grand to set it up for him. I soon slipped into depression, or it had never really gone away, and I retreated deep inside myself. I only surfaced when I rode the horses or spent time with them and when I went on long walks with the cats streaming behind me, silly Spider in my arms. It sounds idyllic, but those walks were blurred by tears coursing silently down my cheeks. It was only a matter of time before it all came crashing down. My money was running out fast. I knew this and was terrified at the consequences of one day there being a big fat zero in the bank.

Hannah had gone back to France so I was alone and in a bizarre turn of events I was contacted on Facebook by two crazy nutters from my past, Roger and Pete, two mad hatters. Roger was cycling down the Portuguese coast and Pete happened to be in Northern Portugal in his camper van complete with potbellied stove. One night, when it was dark and I had finished with the horses, lit a fire and put Tessa to bed, I poured myself a glass of wine and heard an engine. I looked out of the window and there in the distance were two headlamps bumping over the rough ground coming my way. They had arrived.

Straight away they recognised I was not right. They noticed something deeply wrong and talked to me about it. I poured my heart out to them and about my long-term plan that I hoped would work. "Caramello is dying, it's the melanomas, he has them internally and he is losing weight rapidly," I said. "I can't leave without him, and Tessa loves it here and she won't adapt to school back home and I have nowhere to go." The two mad hatters stared at me. I swallowed and continued, "I think if I wait until I'm about fifty years old the horses will have died, I may have finished training the younger ones so I can sell them or give them to good homes and maybe the cats will have died too, because I can't take them home to the UK, they'll never adapt and will get run over because I won't be able to afford a quiet place to live. Then there's Tessa's schooling to think of, she will have finished school by then. So if I wait until I'm fifty maybe I can leave."

To me now this sounds absurd, like it did to them. I was wishing my life away and my animals' lives. I should have been thinking of Tessa. She needed a happy mother, a mother who enjoyed life, one that may even get a chance at love again. This is what Roger and Pete tried to make me understand. They asked about the house and told me to kick the Troll out. It was in my name and I was the mother of his child so I had rights. Then Pete said he would help me build the stables and I could make a go of things on my own. The Troll would have to pay maintenance for Tessa and I would be okay. Hannah would come back and help me too. My English neighbours also agreed this was a good idea. I had friends and support if only I could leave the Troll. So why couldn't I?

I had been trapped by his words for so long, I didn't realise there could be a life without him. The debt in France he'd put in my name was paid off; surely he had no hold over me now? The mad hatters left before the Troll returned and I had renewed hope. I began to see a light at the end of a very long tunnel. Debbie contacted me and said she had sold in Spain and bought a place not far away. She was going to try and make a go of it as a camp site. She still lived at and ran her parent's large and successful camping business in the UK so she had plenty of experience. We could maybe do something together, I could offer trail rides and classical equitation. I'd even started giving some regular lessons again. Things could work. I had a chance.

The Troll's claws

When the Troll returned I announced to him that our relationship was over. He didn't respond, didn't seem bothered. He just looked at me, mildly amused. I stressed it again, thinking he'd not heard what I was trying to say, although I couldn't have made it any clearer. He sat down at his usual place and picked up his laptop.

"Go then, I'm not stopping you,"

"You're not getting it," I said. "I'm staying here because I am the one who takes care of the animals and you are going to move out and get somewhere local. The land across the road is in your name, you could live there." When we'd bought the property it had come in two lots, one plot with the house and main land, and another lovely piece of land not far away with an abundance of well water, olive and orange groves. It was always green and verdant and he made sure it had gone into his name. He was always saying what a fantastic builder he was, he could get a job and make himself somewhere to live there. He was hardly ever at home anyway. It made sense to me.

"You can move out," he laughed. "I'm not going anywhere."

I couldn't believe he would even consider throwing Tessa and I out, but this was not his plan. He slowly informed me that I would be thrown out but Tessa would stay with him. He would never let her go. I thought frantically – I had rights, the house was in my name. I was Tessa's mother, he could not take her from me. Fear begun to rush through my head and spill down my spine like cold water, my breathing accelerated and I felt sick. I tried to cling to the new found confidence I had gained from the two mad hatters.

"The house is in my name. I can get you thrown out," I said. He laughed his horrible high-pitched giggle which grated on my nerves like nails on a blackboard.

"This house is mine," he said. "The money I can prove is mine, and if you play stupid I will reclaim a debt you owe me."

Debt? What was he talking about; I didn't owe him any money. Enjoying my confusion he smiled at me, his expression amused, and stood up. He was very tall, huge in fact, a typical Troll. He liked to speak down at me. Slowly he began to circle me.

"When we bought the house in France in joint names? Do you remember the paperwork we had to sign and you signed a document which I told you meant we avoided paying two lots of taxes?"

I couldn't answer, I couldn't remember much about the last few years but panic and pain. Except there was an awful amount of paperwork to sign and a French notaire present that spoke no English.

He continued striding around me like a lawyer in court confident in his defence. Then he leaned in close. I could smell his unwashed body. My head spun and I struggled to breathe; my fingernails cut into my palms.

"What you really signed is a document that meant I had lent you the money to buy your half of the house and that you have no rights whatsoever to any property, whether it is in your name or not." I was astounded. It was like a punch to the face. "So if you continue with this stupidity I will reclaim the debt and take your inherited half of your parents' house, from you, to repay the debt." His face was inches from mine, then he wiped his hands in front of me in a *washing his hands of me* gesture whilst laughing in that high-pitched giggle.

"What?" I cried. "I don't understand… you can't do that…" But he had done it.

"Oh yes I can, and I will," he said. "It was my family's notaire that drew the document up, I have his contacts." He then went back to sit down before looking back at me. "Go on then, bugger off, but Tessa stays here. Portugal is a patriarchal country and I have sole rights."

I felt like he had repeatedly punched me in the stomach. In fact had he done this, I would have found it easier. He had been physically abusive to me before but had had a fright when he pushed me so hard I fell over backwards, hitting my head and cricking my neck. At first he had accused me of pretending to be hurt, but soon realised he had to take me to the hospital. I remember sitting there in cold stony silence whilst he told the doctor in French all about how a horse had pushed me over. The doctor looked at me and in French asked me if it was true. I nodded and remained silent although inside I was screaming for help. I wish I'd told the truth but I was afraid. The Troll was French and he had told me I was insane and everyone would understand why he acted like that, why I had to be sectioned... because I was mad.

I staggered out of the house and went to see the horses. Caramello wasn't very well these days. He was about 31 years old now, which is very elderly for a horse. He had melanomas which the vet had told me were inside him and were why he was losing weight. I didn't want to leave him but I had to run away, I had to take my child and escape. He nuzzled me and I know he looked inside and read my mind. He had been such a strong and mighty character back in the days of Camelot. It pained me to see him so weak, but his eyes were not weak, his soul would live on in magnificent white fire.

I spoke with Hebraico next. He was another incredible soul I had first met many years ago. He was also an aggressive stallion; I had a knack of dealing with these difficult brutes. They were not really brutes though, especially not Hebraico. A lovable rogue yes, but never a brute. He was in his late twenties now and had never recovered fully from a bout of piroplasmosis. Maybe it was his time to die, here in Portugal. He was in a large field area with lots of grass and well water, away from the other horses as he was so wicked towards them. He was a wonderful horse but his temperament around others was appalling. He had been born in Portugal and his golden dun coat fitted in with the land as the sun set behind the ancient gnarled olive trees. He looked like he didn't want to go anywhere else. He looked like he was home. If I moved though I would have to try to take him, but for the moment he would be fine until I found a solution.

Next I spoke to Wynnie who just dismissed me. He read my mind immediately, time to move on again. My travelling col-oured horse, he would always be with me. Then I spoke to Atomico, such a beautiful talented horse, one I had spent years training, yes he would have to come if I ran. Then there was

Moon, the cremello Spanish mustang, I knew I'd never get him to give her up, it broke my heart to even touch her silky cream hair. She looked at me with her clear blue eyes; she was a mother. She knew what I should do. A flicker of recognition passed through my mind of a pearly horse with eyes the colour of pale weather. I knew then that I had to find a way out, back to where I belonged and away from the Troll.

I wandered around the land; the cats followed me and I picked up their warm furry bodies and cuddled them one by one, my tears dampening their fur. I couldn't go back to the house yet, Tessa was there watching TV, she'd seen enough arguments, witnessed her mother cry far too many times. My mind raced as I struggled to decide what to do. Somehow I had to leave with Tessa, but how? I stopped to stroke my young bay horse, Hechizo or Chi as I called him. He was slowly coming around to accepting me as his person. I had bought him cheaply from an awful Spanish guy using some of my auntie's money. I didn't want to buy him, I needed that money, but Hannah told me he was so lovely and felt so sorry for him and I could retrain him and sell him to a good home in the UK and make more money back, saving him too.

As the sun set the cats disappeared into the shadows; confident hunters they leapt and jumped in and out of the trees heading for the mountains. I could never take them with me; they'd hate the UK and would probably get killed on the roads. I had found them a safe haven here where they could roam, hunt, play and be safe. I would miss them terribly. Then Spider came and snuggled up onto my lap. He didn't like straying far from me; he was a mollycoddled pedigree house cat. He would have to come with me. He looked up at me half blinking his eyes, happy I had understood that he would be coming too.

I didn't sleep that night and the following morning after Tessa had gone to school I decided to confront the Troll and tell him I was leaving with Tessa. I had enough money left from my auntie and knew that if I didn't make a move soon there would be none left and my only chance at freedom would have gone. His response was cold and simple. I could leave but Tessa couldn't and he had the sole rights to his daughter. He had played with my mind so much I didn't know what the truth was anymore. Was this patriarchal bullshit just more lies made up by him to confuse and suppress me?

Having experienced so much emotional, physical, physiological and financial abuse from this man for years I couldn't hear my own voice. People always wonder why I stayed for so long, why any victim of abuse does, but it's like you don't control your thoughts anymore. I fully understand why some people have committed suicide in abusive situations. The fear and anxiety would end and the blissful feeling of nothing would take over. I would be nothing. I wouldn't have to worry about anything anymore because there would be no me... but somewhere hidden in the back of my mind I heard wailing and the mournful cries of a small child.

I was huddled under a tree tearing at my hair unable to open my eyes when Debbie found me. She hadn't even arranged to come, she had just got on a plane and on a whim driven to see the farm she had bought and had called in at my place on her way. I couldn't believe it. I poured it all out to her, though she already knew most of it. As she wrapped her arms around me she told me it was now time. I had to keep going, I couldn't give up now. She then proceeded to go into the house and give the Troll a verbal bashing regarding his patriarchal attitudes. She had lived and run a business in Portugal, spoke the language and knew the laws. She told him he did not have sole rights over Tessa but we had equal rights and, given his past record, the courts were more likely to let Tessa live with her mother.

The Troll was backing down. Although he still threatened me with reclaiming the debt against my name, Debbie told him to just fucking try it because it was probably all more bullshit anyway. For the first time I saw him for what he was: A weak bully that picked on those smaller than him, a nasty being that fed on the fear he created in others. Without this fear to fuel him he had no power, and Debbie had just stripped him of it.

I spent the day with Debbie making plans. Thank God she had turned up. I couldn't wait to also tell my English neighbours that I had decided to leave. Debbie left, making me promise to stay strong and stick to my guns. Coming to Portugal had been the right thing to do. I would take Tessa and Spider in the car and arrange for English transporters to collect Wynnie and Chi and Hebraico later on, once I had found a suitable place back home for Hebraico due to his tendency to want to kill other horses. Caramello would stay, as he was too old and weak to travel; my lovely Portuguese vet told me he would keep an eye on him.

The Troll told me Moon, Atomico, Hades and Apache, the two younger stallions, would stay with him. He made me sign Moon and Atomico's papers over to him. I heard him talking on his phone to a woman I had met in Brittany who doted on him. He said he would be keeping all the horses with pedigree papers. Chi and Wynnie did not have any so I was welcome to them, and he giggled squeakily. He didn't seem bothered about Tessa going with me now. He felt confident he couldn't stop me and I wasn't stopping him from contacting her. In fact I hoped he would continue to stay in touch and visit her with Xmas and birthday presents. Could this really be happening after wanting it for so long?

I broke the news to my family. I was terrified they'd say, *No you can't come home,* which sounds ridiculous, but I felt I needed their permission. They were beginning to realise what the Troll was and how desperate I sounded, because I was returning to Wales regardless. It was my decision and I had made it. The barriers of guilt and shame that held me were broken, the dam had burst and nobody could stop me. I was still their daughter and Tessa their granddaughter and I didn't care what they thought of me – I couldn't take anymore. They could either help me or not. Whatever expectations they had for me, and I had for myself, were no longer important; not to me anyway, and thankfully they helped me

My English neighbours told me friends of theirs, who had a small trailer, were calling, so anything I wanted taking home they would take for a very reasonable price. I managed to get my saddles, and even Tessa's rocking horse, into their trailer. Most of my things, including my Grandmother's dressing table, I had to leave. I took as many of Tessa's toys as I could but she was getting older and would have new ones. The ones that were special I packed. I organised the transporters to pick up the horses and they would arrive two weeks after me. My neighbours had their documents and would deal with that when I had gone. They helped me so much and I owe them my life, but they just saw it as a good deed.

The Troll had begun bragging online about being a classical riding trainer and started advertising for lessons using my photographs to lure people, God help them. He bragged to young French girls on the internet about the horses he owned, inviting them out to help him look after them. He was looking for a new, younger, fool to snare in his evil web.

I still hadn't told him my exact leaving date and I don't think he really believed I would go through with it. Then the internet was turned off and the electricity too because I was not going to pay the bill again; I needed every penny. I had bought lots of feed for the horses so they wouldn't be going without for a while and there was lots of grass around still. The Troll demanded I pay the bill, I told him I wouldn't and ran over to the neighbours. I was ready. I used their internet and booked my ferry ticket for two days time. The car was French registered and illegal in Portugal; I'm not even sure if it had any insurance but it was reliable and the one thing he had allowed me to have, probably because it was illegal. I prayed I would not get stopped but if I did I would just beg for help.

When I returned he again began shouting, demanding I put the electric and internet back on. I refused. He then told me he wanted the house in his name and he would put the land in my name and I would be free to sell it. I didn't trust anything he said but dutifully went along to the Portuguese lawyers that held the house deeds. It would cost about five thousand euros to do this. The Troll expected me to pay this right there and then. I didn't even have that much left of my money and needed every penny for my new life. He yelled and shouted at me but still I refused. He then said he would sell the land and give me the money if I would use it to sign the house over to him. The land was valued at about fifty thousand, a silly figure but even if he got thirty I would agree and we would try and part amicably for Tessa's sake.

The afternoon before I left he asked me for twenty euros, saying I owed it to him. I decided not to argue, but when I came back from the cash point, having withdrawn my money for the journey, he wasn't around so I left it on the table under a heavy cook book. I then finished packing the car and readying Spider and Tessa's things. She was confused, but I had told her we were going to Wales to live and she was excited to see her family again. Her father had frightened her lately, shouting at her to go to her room so he could argue with me and she wasn't unhappy to be leaving him. What was bothering her was leaving the animals although she didn't show it. Even now, I know she still cries because she misses them so much. There are no tears for the absent Troll.

The Troll came up to me and demanded the twenty euros. "It's on the table," I told him.

"No it isn't," he snapped. I sighed and stopped what I was doing and went in to see. It wasn't there where I had left it ten minutes earlier. Only he had gone into the house since I'd walked out. Tessa was playing outside.

"You've taken it," I said. He denied this and began demanding another twenty. I refused to give in this time. Then he began to demand a gold necklace his father had given me as a present. This was worth money and I had hidden it with my neighbours along with my and Tessa's passports because I had foreseen trouble here. I told him I had posted it to the UK already for safe keeping. He went ballistic with me and stormed out, jumping into my carefully packed car, and drove off. I was terrified. My ferry was booked for the following evening. The next morning I had a seven-hour drive to Santander.

I waited, trying to not show my panic in front of Tessa who had come in for something to eat. When he returned, my carefully packed car had been rifled through and my stuff was covered in dust. He had obviously emptied the car and thrown everything in the dirt looking for this necklace. Then he began shouting at me in front of Tessa and demanding the twenty euros again. I quickly pressed my neighbour's contact on my mobile before he knocked it out of my hand. He grabbed Tessa by her arm and hurled her into her bedroom. I heard someone answer the phone. I picked it up and screamed, *Help!* They arrived in a flash.

I don't know what I would have done if they weren't there. The Troll knew he was outnumbered now. Paul was a strong older man and an ex ship's captain. He stood up to him and warned him to back down. Debs, his wife, took me by the hand and told me to dry my eyes. She asked me where Tessa was and calmly collected her from the bedroom. We grabbed our overnight bags and Spider, and spent the night at their house. I was exhausted, but I only had a few hours sleep, as adrenalin coursed through my veins.

Leaving

The morning of my final departure I didn't have time to say my goodbyes to the animals; to be honest, I don't think I could have coped emotionally to do this. I was escaping. My neighbours accompanied me to the house for the Troll to say goodbye to his daughter. She hardly looked at him. Then off I set – my long journey home after so many years had finally begun.

It was a beautiful clear spring day; the summer heat had not yet arrived. I looked in my rear- view mirror as the Gardunha Mountains shrank and became part of the horizon. Slowly it started to dawn on me: I was leaving. Leaving my previous life, and the animals I cared so much about. I glanced at my daughter whose face seemed strangely calm. She saw me looking and she smiled excitedly because to her this was an adventure and she was going to see her grandparents, aunties, uncles and cousins. She was going to get to know her family properly.

The journey to Santander took a little over seven hours. I only stopped once to fill up on fuel and use the toilet on the Portuguese/Spanish border. I was terrified as a policeman peered at me through the car window as I crossed the border. The rest of the journey passed in a daze. I didn't have satellite navigation, just a map I had studied, and I relied on the road signs. Remarkably, I didn't go wrong. Tessa had wanted to listen to a Lady Ga Ga CD all the way. At least it drowned out Spider's disgruntled yowls. I was running on adrenalin now. I was so nervous every time I spotted a police car, frightened they would stop me and tell me I had to go back to the Troll, that I wasn't allowed to leave. Eventually I saw the sign to Santander and knew we were close.

Santander was a gorgeous town; I'd not expected it to be so pretty with a lovely little beach. We stopped briefly for ice cream; I parked the car next to the ice cream seller so I could leave the window open for Spider to have fresh air whilst we stood outside stretching our legs. I was shaking. I'm not sure whether it was fear, excitement or both. I was halfway home. Tessa seemed to be enjoying herself and wanted to stay and play on the beach. Unfortunately we didn't have time but she was equally excited about the big boat we were going to travel on. I secured her back into the car and took a deep breath before getting in myself and heading off towards the ferry terminal.

This was where the fun started. Our passports were fine but there was a problem with Spider's. It was not a big problem, the Spanish passport control officer assured me, but it meant I had to find a vet in the town and get them to stamp the identification bar code. He said I could leave my car and he would show me a short cut into the town with directions to the vet, which I promptly forgot. So off I went with Tessa, holding her tightly in one hand and Spider in his carry box in the other. Amid the throng of people in the town centre I began to frantically ask in my best Spanish (which was non-existent, if I'm honest) where the nearest veterinary centre was. Eventually I was escorted there by a very kind elderly lady who could speak a little English.

There was a queue. I waited and Spider yowled. Worried I'd miss the ferry, I pushed to the front of the desk amidst scowling ladies with Persian cats and pug dogs. The receptionist seemed to understand my pleas and fetched a capable looking lady vet. She took Spider's passport and studied it. I waited... and I waited. Then much to my own surprise and horror – as well as everybody else's – I fell to my knees and sobbed uncontrollably. Not just gentle crying, oh no, these were huge, embarrassing wrenching and wailing sobs. The lady vet looked down at me and rather worriedly assured me that all was OK and I could sail, complete with my cat. The receptionist hurried around the counter to help me to my feet. The lady vet quickly stamped the passport and I was charged fifty euros and rather promptly escorted to the door with more brief directions as to how to get back to the ferry terminal.

"Well that was rather embarrassing," said my daughter looking up at me, unaware as to why her mother had started crying in front of strangers. I laughed a little nervously and Spider yowled.

"Mummy is just a little bit tired after the drive, Tess, I promise I'll not embarrass you again." We both smiled and hand in hand we somehow found our way back to the ferry terminal. All was now fine with the passport and we were one of the last cars ushered on. Spider was to stay in the car in a larger travel box that had a litter tray too. I gave him fresh water from a bottle and topped up his dry food. We both kissed him. I didn't want to leave him but we had no choice and were assured we could pop down and check on him but would have to be escorted.

I was now beginning to feel exhausted; my shaking had stopped thankfully, but we were both starving. I looked at Tessa and said, "Come on, let's treat ourselves to a lovely meal and then check out our cabin."

"Yes!" said Tessa. "And I want the top bunk, okay, Mum?" I laughed and nodded. I'd be happy to sleep on the floor once I'd eaten. I raised a glass of wine to myself as I tried not to think of the consequences of what I'd done. I'd found the courage and the first half was over. The ferry set sail at 9.15pm and arrived at Plymouth the following day at 4.15pm. The crossing was calm. A huge weight seemed to lift from my shoulders as I felt the ferry leave the Spanish coast behind. I slept long and dreamlessly. The next phase of my life and my daughter's had begun.

Hell

I was marched onto a passenger aircraft in handcuffs and flown to Paris. Here I was handcuffed to the wall in the airport police station whilst waiting for an interconnecting flight to Brest in Brittany. The policemen drank their small espresso coffees and ate Magdalene cakes. One kindly offered me a coffee which I declined. My heart was racing as it was, I didn't need caffeine too. Next we boarded a smaller aircraft. My handcuffs were released once the plane was in the air. I began to think about plane crashes, although I found myself strangely detached. I don't think I had enough fear left to worry about a crash. In fact, I believe I may have welcomed one.

On arrival at Brest I was driven, with blue lights flashing, to St. Breiuc. There two Breton policemen took over and the ones from Nice headed back. I believe they must have felt sorry for me because once inside the court building they removed my handcuffs and I was allowed to use the toilet, which was clean and tidy. I spoke to these policemen, trying to tell them I was innocent and hadn't done anything wrong. They looked at me with pity, and the younger of the two told me that the judge was a very good man and I was lucky he had insisted on bringing me here so soon.

My interrogation with the judge lasted six hours. I wept and shook through the whole experience, exhausted. Thankfully, I was given a lawyer and a translator. He was indeed a fair judge, and quickly appeared to realise I was simply a victim and not the perpetrator, as I hadn't wittingly or knowingly done anything wrong. He explained what had happened to me because I still had no idea. Quite frankly I had been framed and set up by the Troll. The house in Brittany had been reclaimed by the bank for the unpaid debts. The Troll had committed fraud by selling it but managing to leave a paper trail that led to me. He had asked me to sign various documents, which I willingly did, hoping the debt would be paid now that the house was sold. I thought it was all being done legally and above board. There had even been a French notaire present, obviously set up or bribed by the Troll.

The judge asked me why I had stayed in such a terrible relationship for so long. He said I would have had help from the authorities. I could not answer him. Why do victims of abuse stay with their abusers? It is a dark and lonely existence. I feared the Troll and the things he'd said to me. He was the one who spoke the language and appeared to be in control. I was the crazy one crying, hunched up in corners rocking to and fro. I believed him when he said he could get me committed. During that time my life was unrecognisable, but I had finally escaped it. The judge appeared satisfied with all I had achieved for my daughter and myself since I'd returned to my home. I was found not guilty and was free to go.

It's strange how you'd think I would have reacted with threats over my unfair treatment. But even though I had countless questions I could say nothing. He even asked me what I wanted to do now, to which I replied: please let me speak with my daughter. They returned my money and handbag and allowed me to call her. Tears of relief poured down my face as she chatted about how excited she was to show me the beach where Susan lived.

"I can't wait," I said. "I've missed you so much." My voice broke as I struggled to compose myself so she wouldn't know how hard I was crying. I was exhausted but could not wait to get on a train or bus or whatever and begin the long journey south again.

"I'm sorry, there is no train tonight," the judge told me. "In the morning a train goes to Marseilles. You need to get that."

"Where is the train station?" I asked.

"It is in Rennes," he replied. "Do not worry, I will drive you there." I was shocked; what a complete turnaround. Even the two policemen who had been guarding me shook my hand and wished me well.

I was exhausted and feeling slightly light-headed as I sat staring through the car window. The trees and hedges of Brittany passed swiftly by. I could smell fine leather upholstery and some kind of leather cleaner or wax. The judge looked at me, smiling. "It is funny, no? You arrive in manacles and you leave with the judge in his nice new Jaguar car." I contemplated what he said and nervously agreed it was funny, although I didn't laugh.

I began my day-long journey, all paid for by myself, including the hotel for the night in Rennes, back to the South. After two long train journeys I got on a bus and eventually arrived at Cavalere Sur Mer. As I got off I could see only Susan waving at me; next to her was a giant blow up turtle. It was Tessa. She had used her own holiday money to buy him to play with in the sea, she had been having a lovely time and thankfully Susan had assured her of my arrival soon, even though she had had no idea when I would be released.

Even though it had been three years since I had finally found the courage and the strength to leave him, I couldn't believe that his actions could still have had such a profound effect on my life. My saving grace had been my complete innocence at turning up for a holiday with my daughter in a country where I was a wanted criminal.

I still don't know why it had taken so long to get away from him. Was it shame? Was I too ashamed to beg my parents for money to help me get home? Was I embarrassed at having failed? Was it the expectation to succeed and be a success I believed people at home had of me?

It was a mixture of all that, including my inability to recognise what being abused is. I was not a stereotypical victim of abuse. I came from the old-fashioned, no-nonsense, just a load of fuss and bother, get on with it school. It was also my extreme love for my animals that had kept me there, my inability to abandon them. This was my greatest weakness, but it didn't mean I was a weak person. I was a strong person who cared about my animals and the consequences of my actions. I was someone who cared, something the Troll was not and never would be capable of.

There are many bridges we must all cross during our life journey, and under these hide evil trolls. Some of us fall prey and some of us are devoured. Others get away relatively unscathed whilst yet more become trapped and bound by the trolls. They lose themselves, believing the lies they are told, until somehow they see the light and find a way to break free. I had been bound in darkness for long enough until eventually I too broke free.

The Troll was later picked up from the farm in Portugal by Interpol. I heard that many of the locals were happy to hear this; people were becoming wise to him. Unfortunately, he only spent a few months in prison before being released; as yet I have heard no other details. I can't help feeling happy that he at least got to spend a couple of months in prison.

Return to the Holy Grail: The House in the Graveyard

I didn't stop on my car journey from Plymouth to my childhood home. It was only about three hours, unlike the seven-hour non-stop haul from Central Portugal to Santander. The most difficult thing was driving on the left, whilst being in a left-hand vehicle. It took all of my concentration. Spider still yowled, although he appeared to have lost his voice and it sounded more of a croak. Tessa, bless her, was being such a good girl and had coped amazingly well. Better than me I believe. I was exhausted and it was a good job I didn't stop for a break or I may never have continued. Soon I turned off the M5 and headed in the direction of south Wales. I couldn't wait for the bridge. It's always been a heart stopping moment for me, and for all Welsh people I think, when they cross from England into Wales. Whether they love the country or hate it, a certain shift takes place deep within the soul.

The motorway curved gracefully towards the tall, pale blue towers and steel cables that hold together the vast structure of the bridge. The aqua colour makes it look soft and fluid, as it stretches languidly across the mudflats and river below. A mackerel sky rippled overhead. I joined the end of a small queue of cars leading to the toll booths and noticed the increase in price. I had no English money so I'd have to use my card. Thank God for plastic I thought, and my poor auntie. Soon I was heading swiftly down the M4 corridor noticing familiar landmarks. I thought back to the time I'd visited home, when I lived in Exmoor.

The new bridge, or second Severn crossing as it is now called, hadn't been completed then. I remembered heading up to the old one watching and waiting for the unveiling of the new. I chuckled, remembering my lovely old Triumph Spitfire sports car. How I loved that car, but it broke down every time I tried to drive it further than Exmoor. My friends and family used to laugh saying the breakdown company would go out of business, the amount of times that car ended up on the back of their lorry. My yearly premium would never have covered the expense.

One time it was an awfully windy night and the rain was

hammering down. I was heading back to Wales for a friend's birthday bash. The little white sports car only had a soft top roof. In summer this was lovely but it leaked terribly in the rain. The old Severn Bridge was closed to lorries because of high winds, but thankfully cars were still allowed. Huddled in what seemed like a cockpit filled with the familiar beats and riffs of Peter Gabriel's 'Salisbury Hill', I sang, confidently belting my voice out, knowing nobody could hear. The singer describes this song as being about losing what you have for what you might get; it's all about letting go – which unbeknown to me at the time, has become a major theme in my life.

The memory of that night was still strong, and I remembered how important that theme resonated with me then too with my internal debate over selling my horse Frostie, so I could explore my dreams and travel abroad. I remember toying with this idea all those years ago as I drove across the swaying bridge. The only thing stopping me then was self-doubt and fear of doing the wrong thing, fear of failure.

The tiny sports car wipers had squealed back and forth, which sounded like the shrieking wind goblins that haunted me. The next minute the terror was all too real. The silly little soft top blew open. I hadn't realised what had happened at first. One minute I was climbing up on Salisbury hill and the next I was being torn and battered by the howling wind. I screamed, but the wind screamed louder. I pulled onto the hard shoulder and struggled to drag the soft top back on. There were levers inside to clip it closed. I convinced myself that I'd not closed it securely and tried to ignore the odd scratches on the outside of the hood. I glanced nervously about; the wind laughed wickedly over the bridge.

My sports car musings were interrupted by the sight of Port Talbot steel works, sitting dark and ominous ahead of me. Ugly and grotesque, it usually made me feel morose, but today was my day. I was coming home and this was another familiar landmark. I began counting down the junctions, getting Tessa to join in too. Soon we left the M4 and merged with the smaller roads that led through the villages surrounding my home. I felt nervous. I'd not thought things through properly. Deep down I knew I'd have to find somewhere to live pretty soon. I was always aware that my parents did not want me staying with them indefinitely. This knowledge had been ingrained into me, ever since I'd moved out at sixteen to work at the hunting and jumping yard. I'd bounced back a few times when younger, but my mother and I always rubbed each other up the wrong way. I had been used to living away during my adult life and coming back seemed like stepping into an old photograph. It felt alien. I'm not sure how my father felt about me coming home either. When I was a child he had always been working, but now he was retired. He'd visited me abroad, he'd always loved that, but now I was a failure. I'd let everybody down. I'd given up. Suddenly, I didn't want to come home. Was there no place else I could run to? But I was almost there, and I was exhausted.

I knew the horses would have to go into the acre paddock my parents owned, and the old empty stables would spring back to life. The paddock was like a golf course these days, my father even rolled it. I had a couple of weeks before they were due to arrive. I was paying an English horse transport company to deliver them. For now I needed to take one day at a time. Home first and a good night's sleep for Tessa and me, and hopefully Spider – that's if he would stop meowing. With a jolt I remembered a text my sister had sent me before I boarded the ferry. She had said not to worry, my mother had seen the perfect place for me to rent. It was pretty much in the village centre, but was attached to an old chapel in a graveyard. I was going to be OK, I had somewhere. I wracked my brain to remember it, and realised it was on the road to the park. I had sat many times in that graveyard as a kid, contemplating life.

I drove down the familiar hill past the old pub that was now a successful Indian restaurant, and there sitting stern and proud on the left was my parent's house. Outwardly, it hadn't changed much since I was a child, but thankfully these days there was central heating. I pulled off the road and onto the driveway, which led into the courtyard. I could see my sister and niece's cars were there. I was unsure how to react. I didn't know what to feel. My relief was almost tangible but self-doubt and paranoia had been my companions for so long now, it was difficult to push them aside. My main priority was Tessa, and she was excited to see her grandparents. I realised my underlying trepidation at being here again was my problem, and I didn't want her happiness to be spoiled by my unease.

My parents appeared on the path coming into the yard. I was terrified of their reactions but their faces beamed. They hugged me and I began to relax. Maybe my demons were losing the game. Had I finally managed to grasp that enamel mug? As my father smiled I realised it was all my own paranoia; the mug wasn't important anymore, and never had been.

I was rigid with nerves from the journey, but slowly began to feel the pressure leave my body. My sister and my niece were delighted at our safe arrival and suddenly it felt as if I had never been away, that it had all been a huge nightmare. I had made it, driven home from central Portugal leaving my old life behind, and I was ready to embark on a new chapter. Spider's insistent yeowls broke through my reverie, and he was promptly removed from the cage and introduced to his Welsh surroundings.

That night Tessa had her own room, and Spider and I were confined to my old childhood bedroom. It had been redecorated with ivory walls, and soft peach furnishings: a far cry from the cornucopia of horse posters, heavy metal album covers and fantasy pictures, including a map of Middle Earth. I put Spider's litter tray in the corner of the pristine room, and felt my uneasiness lift. The familiar stone walls cocooned me, and the unchanged view of the top of the field where the fear wolves had once gathered, regarded me peacefully.

My parents had welcomed me happily and hadn't questioned what had happened. This would take time. I was not yet ready to talk. I realised I had another long journey ahead, but this time an internal healing voyage. I got into bed and melted into the comforting outline of my childhood room. Spider checked out his facilities and after some restlessness and more meowing eventually fell asleep. I lay awake stroking his silky head, staring at the dimly lit walls. My mind was a cacophony of thoughts and I couldn't quite focus on a single one.

The next couple of weeks were hectic. It involved filling in forms for benefit help, as I had no income, and Tessa's father was not prepared to give me a penny. During the years that followed he has never even sent her birthday or Christmas presents. He never contacts her and has simply written her out of his life. He kept the farm in Portugal, which happens to still be in my name, but I am powerless to claim a penny. It is expensive to take somebody to court in a foreign country, especially someone who would burn every single letter they received, causing the cost of taking them to court to further escalate. Also, he claimed that he could prove that his father left him the money, and even though we were together with a child at the time, I had no rights to any of it.

I wanted to put the house in his name, not wanting anything more to do with it. He owned some land opposite the property, which he agreed to transfer to my name so that I could sell it. In true Troll fashion he demanded I pay the fees for the changeover of deeds, which I couldn't afford. So, he said he would sell the land and use some of the money to change the deeds, giving me the rest. Fortunately, I was friendly with the estate agents, and they excitedly informed me that he had sold the land for thirty thousand euros.

I had an email from the Troll stating that the land had sold for a mere fifteen thousand and after paying five thousand to transfer the deeds, Tess and I would be left with only ten thousand. When I questioned him, via Skype, on the fact that the land had actually sold for thirty thousand and that he owed me twenty five thousand, he exploded in anger. I have heard nothing from him since. A source suggested to me that he and his new wife spent the profit in about six weeks, on a holiday in Barcelona and various luxuries.

The farm therefore remains in my name, which helps him enormously, because he can get into as much debt as he likes, but not lose his house. This frustrated and angered me, and still does if I let it. I wished I could donate it to some worthy cause and give them the pleasure of uprooting him but thinking like this made me bitter, and I wanted to be free of negativity. Instead, I kept my thoughts positive and enrolled onto a joint honours English literature and creative writing degree course at the university, something I had never believed possible until now.

My mother and my niece took me to visit the house in the graveyard. Even though it said no pets allowed, my niece kicked me in the shins when I was about to tell the agent about Spider. After the lease was signed I did speak personally to the Reverend, who was now my landlord, and told him about my spoilt Siamese house cat. I was terrified he would be cross and demand that I either leave or get rid of the cat, which was totally out of the question. Tessa had begun jokingly to refer to Spider as her little brother; he was an important part of our family. Fortunately the Reverend was not bothered, and said Spider was very welcome at Ty Capel, which is Welsh for Chapel House.

Ty Capel, the chapel and graveyard, sits on a slight hill encircled by a stone wall. There is a wide formal entrance by the main road, and a smaller one leading from the dead-end road that heads to the park. Our house is attached to the chapel, almost like a naughty child holding its father's hand. Whereas the chapel has an air of authority, Ty Capel exudes a warm and friendly, almost mischievous, manner. The windows with their white paintwork surrounds look like eyes blinking brightly, in contrast to the dark grey stone. I furnished it from second-hand shops and solid old pieces I found in the outbuildings at my parents, things my mum had replaced with new and my Dad had refused to get rid of, so they'd sat in cobwebbed limbo. Now they sat in Ty Capel. My favourite room is my bedroom, it's like a sanctuary. Two floor-length double aspect windows look out over the graveyard and street below. It sits above the other houses, making me feel safe and protected, high in my eyrie.

Tessa was amazed to be living in an actual graveyard. I had been worried about how she would feel to live in a town, when she had been used to such a wild and natural existence far from everyday civilisation. The first eight years of her young life were something many children simply wouldn't understand. She'd crawled across winter-deserted, golden Mediterranean beaches, run wildly through fairy forests in Brittany, and climbed the

Gardunha Mountains of Central Portugal, accompanied by a large black dog, looking like a changeling child. I suppose this normal British way of life was new to her – it was to me, as things had changed since I'd been here last. There was even a Tesco supermarket down the road.

It was a beautiful May evening the first night Tessa, Spider and I spent in the quirky graveyard house. We went for a walk to read the tombstones outside. Spider jumped about chasing grasshoppers and Tessa read the graves with me. Neither of us felt afraid; I told Tessa it's not the dead that hurt you, only the living do that. Cars passed on the main road heading into the village, and people walked their dogs up the lane past the little gate. Not a single person noticed us. We would have been a strange sight if they had. My hair was still long and tangled as I'd not been to a hairdresser for years. Tessa looked like a ragamuffin child and Spider resembled a living grotesque on a lead. Tessa looked up at the tall stark chapel and said, "Mummy, it's called Trinity, doesn't that mean three?" She'd had no religious upbringing from me, but her French and Portuguese language background had helped her work it out.

"Yes, it does," I replied. "Although, they are referring to the Father, the Son and the Holy Ghost," I told her.

"Oh, I don't think so," she said, dismissing my reply. "I think it's a sign, and it means us – you, me and Spider. We were meant to come here." I smiled at her and agreed it was indeed a sign. I thought back to all the times I'd sat in this graveyard as a child, and not once had I ever noticed the name of it. Ten out of ten for observation to Tessa and zero for me. I watched her pick a bunch of orange hawkweed and place them on a grave that had an angel carved into the stone. She looked at me, saying, "There's a mother and a baby in this one, Mummy." I approached and read the stone, it was getting taken over by ivy but yes, there was a young mother and her baby, who'd died in 1901. I said a little prayer for them as Tessa laid the flowers down.

That night Tessa went to bed falling asleep pretty much as soon as her head hit the pillow. She had a new purple metal bed, with pink and lilac bedding. She looked happy. Spider curled up next to her. A weight seemed to lift from my shoulders. It was such a relief to see them safe and content. I went downstairs and opened a bottle of white wine. Time for me to toast my own efforts, I thought, pouring a large glass before putting on the TV my sister had given me. She said she was going to throw it because it was on its way out. I'm glad I stopped her and gave it a home, because it's still working even now. I put my feet up and leant back on my fifty quid leather settee and watched a good old horror film. There's no better place than a graveyard in which to watch a good horror film. For the first time in ages I felt independent – and I loved it.

I awoke the next morning to the sound of gulls mewling and ha-ha-ing outside. It was a sound I'd missed and a sound I loved. Being close to the estuary and not far from the Gower peninsula, Ty Capel is a prime perch for herring gulls and black backed gulls. It is also home to gatherings of jackdaws, a pair of magpies and not to forget Mr and Mrs Blackbird who enjoy sounding their alarm call, to frighten Spider, as they spring out of the yew tree. The graveyard is a hive of wildlife activity. Apart from the birds that steal the blackberries, there is a hedgehog family that munch on the many slugs, squirrels that harvest the hazel nuts, and one night I saw a fox trot through.

There is a magical feeling Tessa and I both get when we step off the road and close the graveyard gates behind us. It's as if we have stepped into a different land, a much quieter one with an air of mystery – a place of twilight. I leave my bedroom window open at night. During the early hours before dawn I tend to wake. There are no noises from the village and road at this time. This is the true witching hour for me. Some nights I hear the graveyard cats. They congregate amongst the graves to discuss leadership. Spider wakes and peeps at them from the safety of the bedroom. They yowl and scream at each other, tufts of hair fly as ears are torn and noses scarred. They scared the life out of me the first time I heard them, like screaming banshees darting around the tombstones.

My Horses

The day had come: my horses were arriving. I wondered if Wynnie would remember being here as a yearling. Chi had never set hoof outside of Spain so this was a big life experience for him. Soon I'd be able to ride the same trails I'd ridden as a child, even gallop across the yellow mountain with Chi my red brown horse, his peat black mane blowing in the wind. The transporter had contacted me to say all was well. The horses had travelled fine and were now about an hour away. The field was an emerald ocean; a fine place for them to recover from the long journey and a marvellous place for Wynnie to retire.

I sat in the upstairs window of my parents' bedroom, looking out of the front window, and waited. To take my mind off inventing disastrous transport scenarios I thought of my childhood. I remembered sitting here with my school friend Tracie, the summer before I left home at sixteen. We were waiting for our boyfriends to pick us up. They were always late. We'd still be sat there over an hour later, our eighties hair gone flat, before we'd see the car pull into the drive. Then our sparkle would return. We'd run past my mum, ignoring her demands to be home before ten and jump into the back of their car to drown in a crescendo of rock music. I didn't love my first boyfriend – he was more like a brother to me – but we were such a great group of friends. His friends became my friends, and still are some of the dearest people in my life.

Suddenly my thoughts were interrupted by the sight of a huge equine transport lorry. It glided slowly past the house, filling the road, and stopped at the end of the drive. I'd given the driver instructions to reverse in. With my heart in my mouth I ran outside to watch its slow and careful backward progress. Every second brought my horses closer to me. They were here. I could hear them stamping inside the lorry. I called out and Wynnie neighed. The ramp was lowered and I peered inside. Down what resembled a dimly lit tunnel mingling with the smell of sweet haylage and ammonia, I recognised the unmistakable whiff of horses – my horses.

There were no others in the lorry – they'd all been delivered and my boys were the only ones left. They looked tiny standing behind the huge padded partitions at the far end of the truck. The driver helped me lead them out. I hugged them and although Chi was a little bit baffled, I could see Wynnie knew he'd come home. Their legs were unsteady, but we walked them around the yard to make sure there were no injuries, before releasing them into the beautiful green paddock.

A little weary at first, they both sniffed the air then, gaining confidence, they snorted, blowing through their nostrils. Wynnie took the lead and approached the containers of fresh water. He splashed his nose around before slurping a mouthful, dribbling it through his lips, then ran into the field to roll. Chi watched him and followed. It was wonderful to see them again. Wynnie finished rolling and bucked before returning to me to ruffle my hair with his nose. Welcome home my travelling soul, I told him. I breathed in their scent, burying my face deep into their necks. They smelt like summer sunshine, spring rain, autumn storms and frozen winters. Every part of my life was entwined with horses.

Exploring the paddock, they danced and cavorted, leapt and spun like wild things. I watched them in awe from the centre as they charged around me. Wynnie's white markings sparkled and Chi gleamed mahogany red in the sun. The circle was complete. My journey was done.

I looked up at my parents' house and saw Tessa looking out of the bedroom window with my mum. I thought it best she stay safe inside in case anything had gone wrong on the journey. She had a huge smile on her face. Later she asked me where her favourite horse was, Atomico – the one he'd made me sign over to him even though I'd spent years training him. He was a pure-bred Spanish horse and worth money, that's the only reason he'd kept him. It was pure selfishness and gave him something to brag about, because he didn't sell him; a friend later saw poor Atomico in the field looking very bedraggled. Thinking about it he could have given her the horse himself. He had a horse transport lorry and could have brought him over as a surprise; he is her father after all. It broke my heart to tell her that Atomico wasn't coming. She didn't mention him again.

Gradually through the summer months the horses settled in. I didn't ride much, as I had so many other things to organise. Tessa rode Wynnie a few times; he's a little too hot for her but I kept her on the *lunge*. She rides very well and sits beautifully. My sister, who hadn't ridden for a few years, rode Wynnie too. I was concentrating on Chi. I needn't have worried about him adapting to life in Wales. He was a star. His character began to develop, and he realised life is fun, and after his Spanish prison he discovered living in a field is fun. He took everything in his stride, even when buses full of stares passed him on the main road. I'm so glad Hannah convinced me he had to be mine.

I've explored the mountain again, and ridden past the dwarf lord's castle. With trepidation I walked down the track, but the stone dwarves were gone, replaced by smart wooden gates. It was autumn. A rowan tree splattered with crimson berries adorned with chirruping starlings caught my eye. It was a magical tree. Something sparkled on the ground. I stopped and dismounted to see what it was. A delicate silver chain twinkled in the mud. I picked it up; the catch was broken but it was still bright, not tarnished. I hung it on the rowan tree in case someone came back to look for it.

As I mounted back up, I heard a little chuckle. I looked to where I'd hung the chain but it had gone. Thinking it had fallen, I scanned the ground, but there was nothing there. A louder chuckle startled me. Chi heard something too; his ears were cocked to the side, listening. Movement caught my eye. A magpie flew out of the tree and joined its mate circling in the cloudless sky. Two for joy, I whispered to Chi, and smiled, stroking his silken neck before easing him into a canter along the mountain trail. Secretly I hoped the chuckle belonged to the old dwarf lord that was now smiling at the silver nestled in his palm.

Even though I had been uncertain about my decision to return home, I knew it was the right thing to do. I may always struggle with self-doubt and guilt, but what's changed is my way of dealing with it. The hardest challenge was when I learned of Caramello and Hebraico's deaths, within a week of each other, not long after I left. There will never be the right words to describe my feelings. I berated myself for not being there for them in their final hours. I beat myself up at not having been strong enough to have Caramello anaesthetised before I left. Why had Hebraico died? I had even found him somewhere to live away from the other horses and was looking to bring him over, but he had never fully recovered from the piroplasmosis. I had been kidding myself... but he had looked so well grazing under the olive trees.

A good friend, who knew them both, told me I should not be upset. He said they were far stronger beings than me and would have hated me watching them die. He told me they had hung on until I had saved myself. Then they had let go, to join me spiritually as they knew they couldn't follow physically. Of course he was right. The vet told me they had both gone downhill after I'd left and it was their time to go. He also arranged the body disposal for me, which was free as my house was registered as a farm. It still didn't stop the Troll asking me for three hundred euros per body to dispose of them, saying that this was the price he had paid.

As the Welsh winter swooped across the shivering country-side, I reflected upon the landscape of my life and how the maze had led me full circle. I'd been everything I could imagine: A centaur warrior friend of the elves who fought dwarves, Alice in an enchanted Portuguese wilderness, Gwenhyfar in medieval Camelot, and a mother battling demons, trying to save her soul. I looked at Tessa as she decorated the Christmas tree; she was excited about her first Christmas in Wales. I was too, so much, that I decided to make a paper horse out of red crepe paper to hang on the tree. I held it up saying 'Ta da!' when I'd finished. Spider batted it with his paw and Tessa laughed; she's much more artistic than me.

"What's that supposed to be?" she asked.

"A paper horse decoration," I told her, "but careful, he'll come alive at night."

"Don't be silly," she giggled, eyeing him suspiciously... but I know she believed me.

Facing the Tower and storm

After the Troll I thought relationships would be easy. I hadn't realised there is a big step from being in your late twenties – when I had met the Troll – young, free and single, to being in your mid-forties and finding you have to start all over again. At first I embraced this feeling. I felt excited and eager to actually start living and find love maybe. It didn't work like that though. Inside I might be a naive twenty-something but in reality I was a damaged forty-something, a magnet for the depressed men, the alcoholics and the narcissists.

All of them just wolves in sheep's clothing, and like the three little pigs I rushed from one to the next looking for a solid foundation to rebuild my life on. The third however, was the wolf that came down the chimney to fall into the little pigs' cooking pot. These fear wolves have haunted me for so long now. I would not run anymore. I would consume the wolf. I would journey deep inside myself directly to the pain. I was angry. Angry for having been through so much only to allow myself to be hoodwinked yet again by false men.

In fairy tales it is always an animal or beast, mythical or not, that aids the protagonist in some way, reveals a certain truth. Real life is not a fairy tale but we still need to learn from it and not follow the same patterns again and again. Maybe that was the wolf's intention for me. I gained my strength from my horses but faced my fear through the wolf and learnt how to deal with it and respect myself again. So I thank these wolves that taught me to change direction and heal my wounds.

I was prescribed antidepressants by the doctor, but not being a pill person I knew they wouldn't work for me. I understand they work for some but this was not going to be my healing card. Instead I got counselling on the NHS. This helped me to accept the reasons why I'd stayed in an abusive relationship with the Troll for so long. It put it all into perspective and helped me to see myself in a different light. I stopped falling prey to these wolves. I began to practice meditation, and during this I made a bee line for the hurt and pain I'd locked away. Sometimes when

I hurt physically, I control my breath and mentally travel to the source of the pain and it slowly dissipates. Now, in my own visual meditation, I had to travel straight to the emotional hurt and clear it once and for all.

I was now the warrior woman on the red bay horse pushing through the wind goblins. I would cross that wasteland, get to the tower, stop the crying and deal with the pain. I would not be weak anymore. The prowling wolves could not stop me now. I would consume any who came near. Inside the tower it was dark except for the faint glow coming from the candle on the floor. Water dripped down the walls. The screeching goblins were silent, holding their breath, their fury useless. I could hear soft strangled sobs coming from a hunched shape. I stood tall, prepared to challenge any kind of monster or demonic beast I would find.

As I crept forwards I raised my gleaming sword and peered into the dark. There on the cold hard ground I saw the huddled shape was a child, the source of the crying. I recognised the jumper, a khaki cream and green woollen one, pulled over beige jodhpurs that covered skinny legs that disappeared below the knees into too big khaki wellington boots. The long dark hair was stuck to the tear-stained face that turned towards me. Arms reached out and the child ran to me. Just like my own daughter when she had fallen would reach unconditionally to me for comfort. I knew then what I had to do.

Placing the sword down I picked the little girl up and hugged her tightly, telling her over and over again how much I loved her. I was crying too now but these were healing tears, they merged with the little girl's tears until they finally turned to laughter. I had learnt to forgive myself, to love and comfort myself unconditionally, something I had never done before but had expected from others.

The other night – and the most significant – marked the coming of the new moon. It had taken a while but it suddenly dawned on me that I was no longer damaged. I felt like I had been cleansed. My life's journey had been mapped by lessons I'd previously ignored, but finally I'd learnt from them. It felt like I was floating in a vast ocean, my cells rejuvenating in the refreshing energy. It was late and cold but I still had my window open. All was quiet and I was just about to drop off when a piercing screech invaded the night. I leapt out of bed and peered through the window. At first I thought it might be the graveyard cats, but this was coming from the sky. It came again, the scream deafening.

I jumped back into bed. Maybe it's an owl, I thought. It certainly reminded me of the screech owls I'd heard at night in Portugal. Then I heard it once more, this time followed by a deep rumbling of thunder. In my mind I pictured a dragon swooping low to announce the approaching storm. Rain began to pour from the previously clear sky. It raced through the guttering, chattering against my window, or was that the grave-yard folk chattering below? Had they left their earthy beds to witness the new moon's arrival, awoken by the storm dragon's screech as it brought the last of the winter storms? One last hurrah before spring's soothing touch arrived to restore and replenish the land. I lay down in my bed, safe and comfortable, listening to the storm and the strange night-time sounds.

My mind drifted back to another storm in France. Lightning had struck the electric fence machine rendering it useless. I was in the kitchen preparing dinner for Tessa when I saw Caramello trot past heading straight for Hebraico's paddock. I ran out of the door, pulling bare feet into boots just in time to see Hebraico crash through his fence too. They would know the minute the electric failed to pulse; velociraptors, the pair of them. Then they clashed together like titans. Mythical beasts, silver against gold, they fought viciously. Hebraico was bulkier than Caramello so had an advantage but Caramello had insanity on his side. I was powerless to stop them and got knocked off my feet like a rag doll to lie bruised on the floor.

As I began to panic, tears streaming down my face, Hebraico, with his superior weight, pushed Caramello to the ground. This was the second I needed to make eye contact with Hebraico. "Get back into your field!" I screamed at him. Incredibly he obeyed me and trotted off, mightily pleased with himself. As Caramello got up, ready for more, I grabbed him by the head collar, and, wrapping the rope rightly round his nose, I dragged him to his stable, shutting him safely inside. I went to get Hebraico who came obligingly, and I shut him in too, in order to check them both for injury. Fortunately neither one was hurt badly, only superficial scrapes and cuts. But it could have been fatal, for me too. Bloody stallions, I thought, it's incredible they both chose to leave this world together.

I closed my eyes and immediately felt my horses... smelt them and became part of them. My beautiful silver demon and golden beast, who had taught me so much, they were with me. I thought about them as I lay contentedly in bed; they are strong and powerful beings, like the storm outside. Caramello is the jagged silver streak of lightning, slicing through the dark, and Hebraico the heavy rumble and crash of thunder, booming in reply. Together they rage through the storm clouds, forever challenging each other, two warriors in the sky. I will always feel their presence in a storm.

Epilogue: The wheel is always turning

My time with the Troll had left me suffering depression with dark suicidal thoughts, but now I wanted to enjoy my life. I had so many reasons to live. In the words of Florence and the Machine, "the dark days are over." I had healed and was a different person. It was during these days of new found confidence that I had embarked on my holiday to the South of France with Tessa and endured that terrible ordeal. It was an ordeal I once again healed from and grew stronger having survived it. The process of writing it all down helped. The pain and confusion is no longer trapped inside but purged onto the page where I can make sense of it and close the book.

Unfortunately, the Troll seemed to have one card left to play, although indirectly. The severe pain in my face from the small lump that had caused me trouble in the prison cell, had been getting worse, some days more than others. I hadn't had another biopsy since I'd returned from my terrible ordeal in France and I could feel something wasn't right. I was on the waiting list for the operation but twice it was cancelled. I kept phoning to enquire and was told priority places were being given to cancer patients.

Eventually I received a call from the hospital and was given a date for the operation. I was extremely nervous, having been told there may be some risk to facial nerves and muscles because the lump was lodged in the top part of the parotid gland basically sitting in a bed of nerves. Debbie refers to it as a baby troll, an accumulation of the suffering and anxieties I went through in France.

The operation entailed cutting across the skin of my neck and up around my ear, then the skin would be peeled back and the lump removed. This way it limited the risk of cutting any of the nerves. Fortunately it was removed with only temporary facial numbness and paralysis but unfortunately, I tested positive for a rare form of cancer. I knew deep down that even though there is no medical proof, I felt it turn malignant during my imprisonment in France. The stress was just too much. My body had managed to condense all the suffering into that one foreign lump that needed to be expelled.

Now it was time to put my life in the hands of my brilliant surgeon and the hospital staff. I had to have extensive scans, including MRI brain scans to check every other part of me. They could not tell me how bad it was until they had all of the results. I spent a terrifying couple of months waiting, believing after everything I had been through I was going to die. After wanting death for so long it was now coming when I wanted to live. I would wake in the night on the verge of a scream. Images of what would happen to Tessa flitted through my mind, all too terrifying to contemplate. Also, what about Spider and my horses? I couldn't abandon my animals again by dying.

Fortunately all my results came back and the cancer had not spread. The amazing surgeon in charge continued to monitor and scan the area. Then a biopsy revealed small traces of cancer still there. A second operation was scheduled in three days. This time they would take out much more tissue, including some skin and anything that the tumour had touched. The operation would now entail cutting straight into my face, which meant I may experience severe facial nerve damage during the excavation – I saw it now as an archaeological dig, removing part of my past – but I didn't care about nerve damage or scars. I would wear any with pride. I just wanted the little beast out of me. I feared the operation and the anaesthetic, but not as much as I feared cancer.

The second operation was scheduled four days after I had the biopsy result. They were moving fast. The night before I had a feeling that I was going to be all right; I was worried, in fact terrified, but somewhere something was telling me I was going to be okay. It was a much shorter operation, leaving me with only twelve stitches this time, instead of thirty two, then, the waiting game again. They needed to test the tissue they had removed before being certain they had got the lot this time. After a nerve-wracking two weeks I was called back in. The surgeon didn't mess around. He smiled at me and told me it was a success. Obviously they would continue to scan and monitor the area for the next five years but the prognosis was looking extremely positive. I was a lucky girl.

After some initial paralysis in my face the nerves soon recovered and I am back to normal. I owe my life to that clever surgeon. The most important thing, after everything I have been through, both good and bad, is that I am a mother and here for Tessa. Neither the Troll nor cancer could take motherhood away from me, and it's been wonderful to see Tessa grow up and find her personality and interests. I fear she will make wrong choices, but all I can do is be there for her. I know that she misses the wildness of her childhood where she ran about like a ragamuffin with two big dogs and a motley clowder of cats in tow, but she'll always have those special childhood memories, just like I have mine.

I still think of my cats that I was unable to bring with me. I pray they had a good life in the wilderness. I dreamt they came to me one night. Misty, who died in Brittany, entered first, followed by Parsley the shy little stray, then Mr. Woody, Phoenix, Mowgli, Snowy and Stormy. They all jumped up onto the bed and curled around my feet. I wasn't in my bedroom but in a wooden cabin. I sat up and stroked them, telling them they were safe and could stay with me now if they wanted to. I was crying, the tears flowing freely. I rose and opened the door to outside. There was a wild and beautiful garden and the sweet scent of roses. The cats yawned and jumped off the bed. As each one passed through the doorway they paused to rub against my bare legs. The sunlight shone into my tearful eyes, blurring my vision into many colours.

I woke at that moment, my arm curled around Spider. I was crying, my face and pillow wet. Spider yawned and stretched, pulling his paws tightly over his face in that cute way that cats do. His pointy Siamese nose peeked between them.

"I'm so sorry, my cats," I whispered. "So sorry I left you." Had they found me now? I have no idea if they are alive or dead. The Troll had claimed to love the cats, although his lack of effort to see his only daughter means he's incapable of any empathy. They should still be living at the farm in Portugal if alive, although I believe they would be quite old now. I knew Misty had died so maybe they all had now and were coming to say goodbye to me before moving on.

The horses from my past will always live in my heart and rest close to my soul and I often think of them all. Each one touched me and taught me something. They fly away from me now like paper cut-outs, confetti in the wind. "I'm sorry," I call out to them. "So sorry I wasn't there for you at the end," but they do not hold any grudges, they forgive me. Horses always forgive and although I know I won't forget my experiences I forgive too, especially myself. It lightens my soul to do so.

Wynnie and Chi are safe and I will always be there for them when their time comes – or maybe they will be there for me. My life has been a journey where I didn't take the straight easy road, or even the steep rocky road, although I may have walked a little way on that. I took the little road in between, the hidden one, which many people miss in life. It winds and twists through the greenwood of legend and spirals into fairy tale.

Wynnie (Haiku)

My travelling soul

Free spirit soars within a

Painted scrap of skin

Hechizo (Haiku)

Chi, my energy

Living breathing magic spell

Nut brown and peat black

The End

About the Author
Julie Ann Rees

Julie Ann Rees holds a first class Masters degree in creative writing from the University of Wales Trinity Saint David. Her short stories have been published both on line at <u>horla.org</u> and in print with Parthian books, Sliced Up Press, Black Shuck Books and forthcoming anthologies with Improbable Press and Honno Press. This is her first book.

She is a single mother and works at a busy rural library in Wales. When not riding her horse over the wild Welsh hills she can be found on:

<u>https://www.facebook.com/julieAnnRees</u>
<u>https://twitter.com/JulieRe36071199</u>

Printed in Great Britain
by Amazon